MATHEMATICS
for Edexcel GCSE
STUDENT SUPPORT BOOK
(WITH ANSWERS)

Foundation Tier

Tony Banks and David Alcorn

Causeway Press Limited

Published by Causeway Press Ltd
P.O. Box 13, Ormskirk, Lancashire L39 5HP

First published 2003

British Library Cataloguing-in-Publication Data.
A catalogue record for this book is available from the British Library.

ISBN 1-902796-53-5

Acknowledgements
Past exam questions, provided by *London Examinations*, *A Division of Edexcel*, are marked Edexcel.
The answers to all questions are entirely the responsibility of the authors/publisher and have neither been
provided nor approved by Edexcel.

Every effort has been made to locate the copyright owners of material used in this book.
Any omissions brought to the notice of the publisher are regretted and will be credited in
subsequent printings.

Page design
Billy Johnson

Reader
Anne Alcock

Artwork
David Alcorn

Cover design
Waring-Collins Partnership

Typesetting by Billy Johnson, San Francisco, California, USA

Printed and bound by Scotprint, Haddington, Scotland

preface

This book provides detailed revision notes, worked examples and examination questions to support students in their preparation for Edexcel GCSE Mathematics at the Foundation Tier of Entry.

The book has been designed so that it can be used in conjunction with the companion book *Mathematics for Edexcel GCSE - Foundation Tier* or as a stand-alone revision book for self study and provides full coverage of Edexcel Specification A and Edexcel Specification B (Modular).

In preparing the text, full account has been made of the requirements for students to be able to use and apply mathematics in written examination papers and be able to solve problems in mathematics both with and without a calculator.

The detailed revision notes, worked examples and examination questions have been organised into 33 self-contained sections which meet the requirements of the National Curriculum and provide efficient coverage of the specifications.

Sections 1 - 10   Number
Sections 11 - 17   Algebra
Sections 18 - 27   Shape, Space and Measures
Sections 28 - 33   Handling Data

At the end of the sections on Number, Algebra, Shape, Space and Measures and Handling Data, section reviews are provided to give further opportunities to consolidate skills.

At the end of the book there is a final examination questions section with a further compilation of exam and exam-style questions, organised for non-calculator and calculator practice, in preparation for the exams.

contents

Number

Algebra

Shape, Space and Measures

Handling Data

Whole Numbers 1

What you need to know

- You should be able to read and write numbers expressed in figures and words.

  Eg 1 The number 8543 is written or read as, "eight thousand five hundred and forty-three".

- Be able to order whole numbers.

  Eg 2 Write the numbers 17, 9, 35, 106 and 49
  in ascending order.
  9, 17, 35, 49, 106

  | Smallest number | ascending order | Largest number |
  | Largest number | descending order | Smallest number |

- Be able to recognise the place value of each digit in a number.

  Eg 3 In the number 5384 the digit 8 is worth 80, but in the number 4853 the digit 8 is worth 800.

- Use mental methods to carry out addition and subtraction.

- Know the Multiplication Tables up to 10×10.

- Be able to: multiply whole numbers by 10, 100, 1000, …
  multiply whole numbers by 20, 30, 40, …
  divide whole numbers by 10, 100, 1000, …
  divide whole numbers by 20, 30, 40, …

×	1	2	3	4	5	6	7	8	9	10
1	1	2	3	4	5	6	7	8	9	10
2	2	4	6	8	10	12	14	16	18	20
3	3	6	9	12	15	18	21	24	27	30
4	4	8	12	16	20	24	28	32	36	40
5	5	10	15	20	25	30	35	40	45	50
6	6	12	18	24	30	36	42	48	54	60
7	7	14	21	28	35	42	49	56	63	70
8	8	16	24	32	40	48	56	64	72	80
9	9	18	27	36	45	54	63	72	81	90
10	10	20	30	40	50	60	70	80	90	100

  Eg 4 Work out. (a) 75×100 (b) 42×30
  $$= 7500$$
  $$= 42 \times 10 \times 3$$
  $$= 420 \times 3$$
  $$= 1260$$

  Eg 5 Work out. (a) $460 \div 10$ (b) $750 \div 30$
  $$= 46$$
  $$= (750 \div 10) \div 3$$
  $$= 75 \div 3$$
  $$= 25$$

- Use non-calculator methods for addition, subtraction, multiplication and division.

  Eg 6 $476 + 254$

  ```
    476
  + 254
  -----
    730
    1 1
  ```

  Eg 7 $374 - 147$

  ```
    3⁶7̷¹4
  -  147
  -----
    227
  ```

  Addition and Subtraction
  Write the numbers in columns according to place value.
  You can use addition to check your subtraction.

  Eg 8 324×13

  ```
      324
  ×    13
  -------
      972
  + 3240
  -------
    4212
     1 1
  ```

  Eg 9 $343 \div 7$

  ```
        49
  7) 3 4 3
      2 8
      ---
        6 3
        6 3
        ---
          0
  ```

  Long division
  ÷ (Obtain biggest answer possible.)
  Calculate the remainder.
  Bring down the next figure and repeat the process until there are no more figures to be brought down.

  Long multiplication
  Multiply by the units figure, then the tens figure, and so on. Then add these answers.

Exercise 1 — Do not use a calculator for this exercise.

1 Write "six hundred and five thousand two hundred and thirty" in figures.

2 Write the numbers 85, 9, 23, 117 and 100 in descending order.

3 (a) In the number 23 547 the 4 represents 4 tens. What does the 3 represent?
(b) Write the number 23 547 in words.

4 Jamie buys these items at the school fair: cola 32p, sweets 45p, pencil 16p.
Find the total cost.
Edexcel

5 (a) What must be added to 19 to make 100?
(b) What are the missing values?
   (i) $100 - 65 = \square$ (ii) $12 \times \square = 1200$ (iii) $150 \div \square = 15$

6 Work out.   (a) $769 + 236$ (b) $400 - 209$ (c) $258 - 75$

7 This table shows the numbers of jars of coffee sold in a shop.

	100 g	200 g	300 g	Total
Ground		50		120
Powder	80	35	26	
Granules	40	45		
Total	135		135	400

Copy and complete the table.
Edexcel

8 (a) By using each of the digits 8, 5, 2 and 3 write down
   (i)   the smallest four-digit number,   (ii)   the largest four-digit number.
(b) What is the answer when you subtract the smallest number from the largest number?

9 The chart shows the distances in kilometres between some towns.
Tony drives from Poole to Bath and then from Bath to Selby.
(a) How far does Tony drive?

Jean drives from Poole to Woking
and then from Woking to Selby.
(b) Whose journey is longer?
   How much further is it?

	Bath			
	104	Poole		
	153	133	Woking	
	362	452	367	Selby

10 Work out.   (a) 200×60 (b) $40\,000 \div 80$ (c) 25×7 (d) $45 \div 3$

11 Petrol costs 72p per litre. Work out the cost of 12 litres.
Edexcel

12 Last year Mr Alderton had the following household bills.

Gas	£364	Electricity	£158	Telephone	£187
Water	£244	Insurance	£236	Council Tax	£983

He paid the bills by 12 equal monthly payments. How much was each monthly payment?

13 A supermarket orders one thousand two hundred tins of beans.
The beans are sold in boxes of twenty-four. How many boxes of beans are ordered?

14 Car Hire Co. have the following cars available to rent.

Model	Number of cars	Weekly rental
Corsa	10	£210
Astra	12	£255
Zafira	6	£289

Work out the total weekly rental when all the cars are hired.

Whole Numbers 2

What you need to know

- Know the order of operations in a calculation.

First	Brackets and Division line
Second	Divide and Multiply
Third	Addition and Subtraction

Eg 1 $4 + 2 \times 6 = 4 + 12 = 16$

Eg 2 $9 \times (7 - 2) + 3 = 9 \times 5 + 3 = 45 + 3 = 48$

- A number can be rounded to an **approximate** number.

- How to **round** to the nearest 10, 100, 1000.

  Eg 3 Write 6473 to   (a) the nearest 10,   (b) the nearest 100,   (c) the nearest 1000.
  (a) 6470   (b) 6500   (c) 6000

- In real-life problems a rounding must be used which gives a commonsense answer.

  Eg 4 Doughnuts are sold in packets of 6. Tessa needs 20 doughnuts for a party.
  How many packets of doughnuts must she buy?

  $20 \div 6 = 3.33\ldots$ This should be rounded up to 4. So, Tessa must buy 4 packets.

- How to approximate to one **significant figure**.

  - Identify the most significant figure.
  - Look at the next figure to the right of this and
    if the figure is 5 or more round up,
    if the figure is less than 5 round down.
  - Add noughts, as necessary, to preserve place value.

  Eg 5 Write each of these numbers
  correct to 1 significant figure.

  (a) 365   (b) 82

  (a) 400   (b) 80

- You should be able to use approximations to
  estimate that the actual answer to a calculation
  is of the right order of magnitude.

  Eg 6 Use approximations to estimate $\dfrac{51 \times 572}{98}$.

  $\dfrac{51 \times 572}{98} = \dfrac{50 \times 600}{100} = 300$

  Estimation is done by approximating
  every number in the calculation to
  one significant figure.
  The calculation is then done using
  the approximated values.

- Be able to use a calculator to check answers to calculations.

Exercise 2   Do not use a calculator for this exercise.

1 Work out.   (a) $6 + 4 \times 3$ (b) $96 \div (3 + 5)$ (c) $2 \times (18 - 12) - 4$

2 Write the result shown on the calculator display
(a) to the nearest whole number,
(b) to the nearest ten,
(c) to the nearest hundred.

$$626.47$$

3 The number of people at a football match was 8681.
Write down 8681 correct to the nearest hundred.

Edexcel

4 A newspaper's headline states: "20 000 people attend concert".
The number in the newspaper is given to the nearest thousand.
What is the smallest possible attendance?

5 The diagram shows the distances between towns A, B and C.

A ●←————————— 287 km —————————→● B ←——— 114 km ———→● C

By rounding each of the distances given to the nearest hundred, estimate the distance between A and C.

6 On Saturday a dairy sold 2975 litres of milk at 42 pence per litre.
By rounding each number to one significant figure, estimate the amount of money received from the sale of milk, giving your answer in pounds.

7 Socks cost £2.85 a pair.
Afzal has £15.
Afzal estimates in his head how many pairs of socks he could buy for £15.
(a) Write down a sum he could do in his head.
(b) Use your sum to estimate how many pairs of socks Afzal could buy.   Edexcel

8 Show how you could find an estimate for $2019 \div 37$.

9 (a) Write down two numbers you could use to get an approximate answer to 41×89.
(b) Work out your approximate answer.
(c) Work out the difference between your approximate answer and the exact answer.   Edexcel

10 (a) To estimate 97×49 Charlie uses the approximations 100×50.
Explain why his estimate will be larger than the actual answer.
(b) To estimate $1067 \div 48$ Patsy uses the approximations $1000 \div 50$.
Will her estimate be larger or smaller than the actual answer?
Give a reason for your answer.

11 A concert hall has 22 rows of seats. Each row has 69 seats.
(a) Work out an approximate answer to the total number of seats in the concert hall.

Every person attending a concert pays £9.75 on entry. Every seat in the concert hall is filled.
(b) Work out the approximate amount of money taken at the concert hall.   Edexcel

12 Tickets for a concert cost £9 each. Ramana has £50.
Work out the greatest number of tickets that Ramana can buy.   Edexcel

13 Melanie needs 200 crackers for an office party.
The crackers are sold in boxes of 12.
How many boxes must she buy?

14 Clint has to calculate $\dfrac{414 + 198}{36}$.
He calculates the answer to be 419.5.
By rounding each number to one significant figure estimate whether his answer is about right.
Show all your working.

15 (a) Find an approximate value of $\dfrac{21 \times 58}{112}$.
(b) Use a calculator to find the difference between your approximate value and the exact value.

16 In 2001 Mr Symms drove 8873 kilometres.
His car does 11 kilometres per litre.
Petrol costs 69.9 pence per litre.
(a) By rounding each number to one significant figure, estimate the amount he spent on petrol.
(b) Without any further calculation, explain why this estimate will be larger than the actual amount.

What you need to know

- You should be able to write decimals in order by considering place value.

  Eg 1 Write the decimals 4.1, 4.001, 4.15, 4.01, and 4.2
  in order, from the smallest to the largest.
  4.001, 4.01, 4.1, 4.15, 4.2

- Be able to use non-calculator methods to add and subtract decimals.

  Eg 2 2.8 + 0.56

  $$
  \begin{array}{r}
  2.8 \\
  + \ 0.5\,6 \\
  \hline
  3.3\,6 \\
  \hline
  {\scriptstyle 1}
  \end{array}
  $$

  Eg 3 9.5 − 0.74

  $$
  \begin{array}{r}
  {\scriptstyle 8,\,14\,1} \\
  9.5\,0 \\
  - \ 0.7\,4 \\
  \hline
  8.7\,6 \\
  \hline
  \end{array}
  $$

  > **Addition and Subtraction**
  > Keep the decimal points in a vertical column.
  > 9.5 can be written as 9.50.

- You should be able to multiply and divide decimals by powers of 10 (10, 100, 1000, ...)

  Eg 4 Work out.
  (a) 6.7 × 100
  = 670
  (b) 0.35 × 10
  = 3.5
  (c) 5.4 ÷ 10
  = 0.54
  (d) 4.6 ÷ 100
  = 0.046

- Be able to use non-calculator methods to multiply and divide decimals by other decimals.

  Eg 5 0.43 × 5.1

  $$
  \begin{array}{rl}
  0.4\,3 & (2\,\text{d.p.}) \\
  \times \quad 5.1 & (1\,\text{d.p.}) \\
  \hline
  4\,3 & \leftarrow 43 \times 1 \\
  + \ 2\,1\,5\,0 & \leftarrow 43 \times 50 \\
  \hline
  2.1\,9\,3 & (3\,\text{d.p.})
  \end{array}
  $$

  > **Multiplication**
  > Ignore the decimal points and multiply the numbers.
  > Count the total number of decimal places in the question.
  > The answer has the same total number of decimal places.

  Eg 6 1.64 ÷ 0.2

  $$\frac{1.64}{0.2} = \frac{16.4}{2} = 8.2$$

  > **Division**
  > It is easier to divide by a whole number than by a decimal.
  > So, multiply the numerator and denominator by a power of 10 (10, 100, ...) to make the dividing number a whole number.

- You should be able to change decimals to fractions.

  Eg 7
  (a) $0.2 = \frac{2}{10} = \frac{1}{5}$
  (b) $0.65 = \frac{65}{100} = \frac{13}{20}$
  (c) $0.07 = \frac{7}{100}$

- How to approximate using **decimal places**.

  > Write the number using one more decimal place than asked for.
  > Look at the last decimal place and
  > - if the figure is 5 or more round up,
  > - if the figure is less than 5 round down.

  Eg 8 Write the number 3.649 to
  (a) 2 decimal places,
  (b) 1 decimal place.

  (a) 3.65
  (b) 3.6

- You should be able to use decimal notation for money and other measures.

- Be able to carry out a variety of calculations involving decimals.

Do not use a calculator for questions 1 to 10.

1 Look at this collection of numbers.
   (a)   Which number is the largest?
   (b)   Which number is the smallest?
   (c)   Write the numbers in ascending order.
   (d)   Two of these numbers are multiplied together.
          Which two numbers will give the smallest answer?

13.5   0.065   0.9   4.5   23.0

2 Work out.   (a) $12.08 + 6.51$ (b) $6.8 + 4.57$ (c) $4.7 - 1.8$ (d) $5.0 - 2.3$

3 Toyah buys the following vegetables.
          0.55 kg onions   1.2 kg carrots   2.5 kg potatoes   0.65 kg leeks
   What is the total weight of the vegetables?

4
   A tin of paint costs £8.99
   Find the total cost of 3 tins of paint.

   Edexcel

5 Henry bought 2 pencils at 28p each, 4 pads of paper at £1.20 each and 1 magazine at £2.95.
   He paid with a £10 note. How much change should Henry get from £10?   Edexcel

6 (a)   Multiply   3.2 by 100.   (b)   Divide   3.2 by 10.

7 (a)   Work out   [700×0.8]   in your head.   Explain your method.

   (b)   Work out   [$60 \div 0.4$]   in your head.   Explain your method.

8 Joseph did the following calculation: $28 \div 8.5 = 3.2$
   (a)   Write down the multiplication which Joseph could do to **check** his answer.
   (b)   Was Joseph's answer correct? Show your working.   Edexcel

9 Work out.   (a)   (i) 13.4×0.3 (ii) 4.8×2.5 (b)   (i) $54.4 \div 0.4$ (ii) $0.294 \div 12$

10 Using the calculation   [$23 \times 32 = 736$] , work out the following.
   (a) 2.3×3.2 (b) $73.6 \div 23$ (c) $736 \div 3.2$

11 Tim paid £5.44 for 17 pencils. Each pencil costs the same. Work out the cost of each pencil.
   Edexcel

12 Write as a fraction.   (a)   0.3   (b)   0.03   (c)   0.33

13 Kevin is working out the time needed to complete a journey.

   Using his calculator, he gets the answer   [0.66666666]
   The result is in hours.
   How many minutes will the journey take?

14 Two pieces of wood of length 0.75 m and 2.68 m are sawn from a plank 5 m long.
   What length of wood is left?

15 Potatoes are sold in bags and sacks.
   Bags of potatoes weigh 2.5 kg and cost 95 pence.
   Sacks of potatoes weigh 12 kg and cost £3.18.
   How much, per kilogram, is saved by buying sacks of potatoes instead of bags of potatoes?

16 Calculate $97.2 \div 6.5$.
   Give your answer correct to   (a)   two decimal places,   (b)   one decimal place.

17 Apples cost 99p per kilogram. Work out the total cost of 3.65 kg of apples.   Edexcel

Working with Number

What you need to know

- **Multiples** of a number are found by multiplying the number by   1,   2,   3,   4,   …

  Eg 1   The multiples of 8 are $1 \times 8 = 8$, $2 \times 8 = 16$, $3 \times 8 = 24$, $4 \times 8 = 32$,   …

- **Factors** of a number are found by listing all the products that give the number.

  Eg 2 $1 \times 6 = 6$ and $2 \times 3 = 6$.   So, the factors of 6 are: 1,   2,   3   and   6.

- The **common factors** of two numbers are the numbers which are factors of **both**.

  Eg 3   Find the common factors of 16 and 24.
  Factors of 16 are: 1,   2,   4,   8,   16.
  Factors of 24 are: 1,   2,   3,   4,   6,   8,   12,   24.
  Common factors of 16 and 24 are: 1,   2,   4,   8.

- An expression such as $5 \times 5 \times 5$ can be written in a shorthand way as 5^3.
  This is read as   '5 to the power of 3'.

- Numbers raised to the power of 2 are **squared**.

  > **Square numbers** are whole numbers squared.
  > The first few square numbers are: 1,   4,   9,   16,   25,   36,   …

  Squares can be calculated using the $\boxed{x^2}$ button on a calculator.

  Eg 4   (a) $4^2 = 4 \times 4 = 16$
  (b)   Calculate 2.6^2.
  Enter the sequence: $\boxed{2}$ $\boxed{.}$ $\boxed{6}$ $\boxed{x^2}$.   So $2.6^2 = 6.76$

- The opposite of squaring a number is called finding the **square root**.
  Square roots can be calculated using the $\boxed{\sqrt{}}$ button on a calculator.

  Eg 5   The positive square root of 9 is 3. This can be written as $\sqrt{9} = 3$.

- Numbers raised to the power of 3 are **cubed**.

  > **Cube numbers** are whole numbers cubed.
  > The first few cube numbers are: 1,   8,   27,   64,   125,   …

  Eg 6 $4^3 = 4 \times 4 \times 4 = 64$

- **Powers**
  The squares and cubes of numbers can be worked out on a calculator by using the $\boxed{x^y}$ button.
  The $\boxed{x^y}$ button can be used to calculate the value of a number x raised to the power of y.

  Eg 7   Calculate 2.6^3.
  Enter the sequence: $\boxed{2}$ $\boxed{.}$ $\boxed{6}$ $\boxed{x^y}$ $\boxed{3}$ $\boxed{=}$.   So $2.6^3 = 17.576$

- The **reciprocal** of a number is the value obtained when the number is divided into 1.
  Reciprocals can be found using the $\boxed{\frac{1}{x}}$ button on a calculator.

  Eg 8   The reciprocal of 2 is given by $1 \div 2 = \frac{1}{2}$.

  On a calculator, enter the sequence: $\boxed{2}$ $\boxed{\frac{1}{x}}$, which gives 0.5.

- Square roots can be found using a method called **trial and improvement**.

  When using trial and improvement: Work methodically using trials first to the nearest whole number, then to one decimal place etc. Do at least one trial to one more decimal place than the required accuracy to be sure of your answer.

- You should be able to use a calculator to solve a variety of problems.

Exercise 4   Do not use a calculator for questions 1 to 9.

1 From the numbers in the cloud, write down
   (a)   those numbers that 2 will divide into exactly,
   (b)   those numbers that 10 will divide into exactly,
   (c)   the number which is double one of the other numbers.

25   27   12
35   30   20
24   100   9   13

Edexcel

2 Look at these numbers: 2   5   8   11   14   17   20
   (a)   Which of these numbers are odd numbers?
   (b)   Which of these numbers are factors of 10?
   (c)   Which of these numbers is a multiple of 10?

3 (a)   Write down a multiple of 7 between 30 and 40.
   (b)   Write down all the factors of 18.
   (c)   Find the common factors of 18 and 24.

4 A number of counters can be grouped into 2's, 3's and 4's.
   Find the smallest possible number of counters.

5 What is   (a)   the square of 4,   (b)   the square root of 81,   (c)   the cube of 2?

6 Write down the value of   (a) $\sqrt{25}$,   (b)   the cube of 4.
                                                                     Edexcel

7 Look at these numbers: 11   15   27   36   44   51   64
   (a)   Which of these numbers are square numbers?
   (b)   Which of these numbers is both a square number and a cube number?
   (c)   Which of these numbers has only two factors?

8 Work out.   (a) $2^3 \times 3^2$ (b) $\sqrt{25} + \sqrt{144}$ (c) $\sqrt{49} \times 4^2$

9 (a)   Which is smaller $\sqrt{225}$ or 3^3?   Show your working.
   (b)   What is the reciprocal of 4?

10 (a)   Between which two consecutive whole numbers does $\sqrt{70}$ lie?
   (b)   Use a trial and improvement method to find the square root of 70
       correct to two decimal places. Show your working clearly.

11 (a)   Find the reciprocal of 7. Give your answer correct to two decimal places.
   (b)   Find the square of 5.6.

12 Use a calculator to work out $15.2 \times \sqrt{10.24} - 3.62$.
                                                              Edexcel

13 Use your calculator to find the value of $5.43 \times \sqrt{(18 - 6.67)}$.
   (a)   Write down all the figures on your calculator display.
   (b)   Write your answer to part (a) correct to 2 decimal places.
                                                           Edexcel

14 (a)   Work out the value of 5^3.
   (b)   (i)   Work out the value of $\sqrt{(4.5^2 - 0.5^3)}$.
           Write down all the figures on your calculator display.
      (ii)   Write your answer correct to 2 decimal places.
                                                               Edexcel

Negative Numbers

What you need to know

- You should be able to use **negative numbers** in context, such as temperature, bank accounts.

- Realise where negative numbers come on a **number line**.

$$-5 \quad -4 \quad -3 \quad -2 \quad -1 \quad 0 \quad 1 \quad 2 \quad 3 \quad 4 \quad 5 \quad 6$$

As you move from left to right along the number line the numbers become bigger.	As you move from right to left along the number line the numbers become smaller.

- Be able to put numbers in order (including negative numbers).

  Eg 1 Write the numbers 19, −3, 7, −5 and 0 in ascending order.
  $-5, \quad -3, \quad 0, \quad 7, \quad 19$

- Add (+), subtract (−), multiply (×) and divide (÷) with negative numbers.

  Eg 2 Work out.
(a) $-3 + 10$	(b) $-5 - 7$	(c) -4×5	(d) $-12 \div 4$
$= 7$	$= -12$	$= -20$	$= -3$

Exercise 5

Do not use a calculator for this exercise.

1 What temperatures are shown by these thermometers?

(a)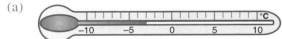

(b)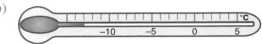

2 The midday temperatures in three different places on the same day are shown.

Moscow −7°C	Oslo −9°C	Warsaw −5°C

(a) Which place was coldest?   (b) Which place was warmest?

3 The top of a cliff is 125 m above sea level.
The bottom of the lake is 15 m below sea level.
How far is the bottom of the lake below the
top of the cliff?

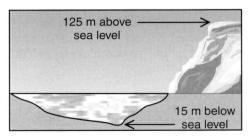

4 Place the following numbers in order of size, starting with the smallest.
$$17 \quad -9 \quad -3 \quad 5 \quad 0 \quad 7$$

5 Work out. (a) $-5 + 10$ (b) $-10 - 5$ (c) -5×10 (d) $-10 \div 5$

6 What number must be placed in the box to complete each of the following?
(a) $-4 + \square = 2$ (b) $-2 - \square = -7$ (c) $\square \times 4 = -12$

7 The table shows temperatures at midnight and midday on one day in five cities.

City	Midnight temperature	Midday temperature
Belfast	−1°C	6°C
Cardiff	−2°C	4°C
London	−8°C	2°C
York	−5°C	3°C
Aberdeen	−6°C	5°C

(a) Which city had the lowest midnight temperature?
(b) At midnight how many degrees higher was the temperature in Belfast than York?
(c) Which city had the greatest rise in temperature from midnight to midday?
(d) Which city had the smallest rise in temperature from midnight to midday?   Edexcel

8 Gordon has £28 in his bank account.
He pays a bill of £85 by cheque, which is accepted by his bank.
What is the new balance in his account?

9 The table shows the temperatures recorded at a ski resort one day in February.

Time	0600	1200	1800	2400
Temperature (°C)	−3	3	−2	−6

(a) By how many degrees did the temperature rise between 0600 and 1200?
(b) During which six-hourly period was the maximum drop in temperature recorded?

10 One evening last winter the temperature in Cardiff was 3°C, in Belfast was −4°C and in Edinburgh was −10°C.
(a) Work out the difference in temperature between
    (i) Cardiff and Belfast,   (ii) Edinburgh and Belfast.
(b) The temperature in Belfast increased by 6°C. Work out the new temperature in Belfast.
(c) The temperature in Edinburgh fell by 5°C. Work out the new temperature in Edinburgh.
                                                                            Edexcel

11 Find the missing numbers so that each row adds up to 5.

(a) | −2 | 3 | | (b) | −2 | | −4 | (c) | | 9 | −1 |

12 The ice cream is stored at −25°C.
How many degrees is this below the
required storage temperature?

ICE CREAM
Store below
−18°C

13 This rule can be used to estimate the temperature in °F for temperatures given in °C.

> Multiply the temperature in °C by 2 and add 30.

Use this rule to estimate −5°C in °F.

14 A test has 12 questions.

> A correct answer scores +3 marks.
> An incorrect answer scores −1 mark.

Pippa attempts every question and scores 8 marks.
How many correct answers did she get?

Negative Numbers

What you need to know

- The top number of a fraction is called the **numerator**, the bottom number is called the **denominator**.

- Fractions which are equal are called **equivalent fractions**.

  To write an equivalent fraction:
  Multiply the numerator and denominator by the **same** number.

  Eg 1 $\dfrac{1}{4} = \dfrac{1 \times 3}{4 \times 3} = \dfrac{1 \times 5}{4 \times 5}$

  $\dfrac{1}{4} = \dfrac{3}{12} = \dfrac{5}{20}$

- Fractions can be **simplified** if both the numerator and denominator can be divided by the **same number**. This is sometimes called **cancelling**.

  Eg 2 Write the fraction $\dfrac{20}{28}$ in its simplest form.

  $\dfrac{20}{28} = \dfrac{20 \div 4}{28 \div 4} = \dfrac{5}{7}$

  Divide both the numerator and denominator by the largest number that divides into them both.

- $2\dfrac{1}{2}$ is an example of a **mixed number**. It is a mixture of whole numbers and fractions.

- $\dfrac{5}{2}$ is an **improper** (or '**top heavy**') fraction.

- Fractions must have the **same denominator** before **adding** or **subtracting**.

  Eg 3 Work out.

  (a) $\dfrac{3}{4} + \dfrac{2}{3} = \dfrac{9}{12} + \dfrac{8}{12} = \dfrac{17}{12} = 1\dfrac{5}{12}$

  (b) $\dfrac{4}{5} - \dfrac{1}{2} = \dfrac{8}{10} - \dfrac{5}{10} = \dfrac{3}{10}$

  Add (or subtract) the numerators only. When the answer is an improper fraction change it into a mixed number.

- You should be able to multiply and divide fractions.

  Eg 4 Work out.

  (a) $\dfrac{3}{4} \times 12 = \dfrac{3}{\cancel{4}} \times \dfrac{\cancel{12}^{3}}{1} = \dfrac{9}{1} = 9$

  The working can be simplified by dividing a numerator and a denominator by the same number.

  (b) $\dfrac{3}{4} \times \dfrac{1}{3} = \dfrac{\cancel{3}^{1}}{4} \times \dfrac{1}{\cancel{3}_{1}} = \dfrac{1}{4}$

  (c) $\dfrac{4}{5} \div 6 = \dfrac{\cancel{4}^{2}}{5} \times \dfrac{1}{\cancel{6}_{3}} = \dfrac{2}{15}$

  Dividing by 6 is the same as multiplying by $\dfrac{1}{6}$.

- All fractions can be written as decimals.

  To change a fraction to a decimal divide the **numerator** by the **denominator**.

  Eg 5 Change $\dfrac{4}{5}$ to a decimal.

  $\dfrac{4}{5} = 4 \div 5 = 0.8$

Exercise 6   Do not use a calculator for this exercise.

1 (a) What fraction of this rectangle is shaded?

(b) Copy and shade $\dfrac{2}{3}$ of this rectangle.

2 Each of these pairs of fractions are equivalent. In each case find the value of n.

(a) $\dfrac{3}{5}$ and $\dfrac{n}{15}$

(b) $\dfrac{n}{3}$ and $\dfrac{8}{12}$

(c) $\dfrac{6}{8}$ and $\dfrac{15}{n}$

3 Which of these fractions are **not** equal to $\dfrac{1}{4}$?

$$\dfrac{2}{8} \qquad \dfrac{3}{9} \qquad \dfrac{4}{16} \qquad \dfrac{6}{24} \qquad \dfrac{7}{35}$$

4 (a) Which of the fractions $\dfrac{7}{10}$ or $\dfrac{4}{5}$ is the smaller? Explain why.

(b) Write down a fraction that lies halfway between $\dfrac{1}{3}$ and $\dfrac{1}{2}$.

5 Write these fractions in order of size, with the smallest first. $\quad \dfrac{2}{5} \qquad \dfrac{3}{8} \qquad \dfrac{1}{4} \qquad \dfrac{7}{20}$

6 Work out $\dfrac{1}{5}$ of £40.

7 This rule can be used to change kilometres into miles.

> Multiply the number of kilometres by $\dfrac{5}{8}$

Flik cycles 24 kilometres. How many miles is this?

8 Jan uses $\dfrac{3}{4}$ of a jar of cherries to make a cheesecake.

How many jars of cherries does she need to buy to make 10 cheesecakes?

9 An examination is marked out of 48.
Ashley scored 32 marks.
What fraction of the total did he score?
Give your answer in its simplest form.

10 The cake stall at a school fete has 200 fairy cakes for sale.

It sells $\dfrac{3}{5}$ of them at 25p each and the remainder at 20p each.

How much money does the stall get from selling fairy cakes?

11 George buys $\dfrac{1}{4}$ kg of jellies at £3.60 per kilogram and $\dfrac{1}{5}$ kg of toffees at £4.80 per kilogram.
How much change does he get from £5?

12 Ann wins £160. She gives $\dfrac{1}{4}$ of £160 to Pat, $\dfrac{3}{8}$ of £160 to John and £28 to Peter.
What fraction of the £160 does Ann keep? Give your fraction in its simplest form. *Edexcel*

13 Work out.

(a) $\dfrac{3}{10} + 1\dfrac{4}{5}$

(b) $\dfrac{5}{8} - \dfrac{1}{2}$

(c) $\dfrac{2}{3} \times 24$

(d) $\dfrac{3}{4} \div 2$

(e) $\dfrac{4}{5} \times \dfrac{1}{2}$

14 Write these fractions as decimals.

(a) $\dfrac{1}{4}$

(b) $\dfrac{7}{10}$

(c) $\dfrac{3}{5}$

(d) $\dfrac{1}{8}$

15 Work out $\dfrac{2}{5}$ of 6.

16 Debra spends $\dfrac{1}{3}$ of her pay on housekeeping, $\dfrac{2}{5}$ on travel and entertainment and saves the rest.
What fraction of her pay does she save?

17 $\dfrac{2}{5}$ of the people at a party are girls, $\dfrac{1}{4}$ of the girls are wearing fancy dress.
What fraction of the people at the party are girls wearing fancy dress?

18 Stuart pays £3 for $\dfrac{1}{4}$ kg of Stilton Cheese and $\dfrac{1}{2}$ kg of Cheddar Cheese.
Stilton Cheese costs £6.40 per kilogram. How much per kilogram is Cheddar Cheese?

Percentages ●●●●●●●●●●●●●●

What you need to know

- 10% is read as '10 percent'. 'Per cent' means out of 100. 10% means 10 out of 100.

- A percentage can be written as a fraction, 10% can be written as $\frac{10}{100}$.

- To change a decimal or a fraction to a percentage: **multiply by 100**.

  Eg 1 Write as a percentage (a) 0.12 (b) $\frac{8}{25}$

  (a) $0.12 \times 100 = 12\%$ (b) $\frac{8}{25} \times 100 = 32\%$

- To change a percentage to a fraction or a decimal: **divide by 100**.

  Eg 2 Write 18% as (a) a decimal, (b) a fraction.

  (a) $18\% = 18 \div 100 = 0.18$ (b) $18\% = \frac{18}{100} = \frac{9}{50}$

- How to express one quantity as a percentage of another.

  Eg 3 Write 30p as a percentage of £2.

  $\frac{30}{200} \times 100 = 30 \times 100 \div 200 = 15\%$

  > Write the numbers as a fraction, using the same units.
  > Change the fraction to a percentage.

- You should be able to use percentages to solve a variety of problems.

- Be able to find a percentage of a quantity.

  Eg 4 Find 20% of £64.
  £64 ÷ 100 = £0.64
  £0.64 × 20 = £12.80

  > 1. Divide by 100 to find 1%.
  > 2. Multiply by the percentage to be found.

- Be able to find a percentage increase (or decrease).

  Eg 5 Find the percentage loss on a micro-scooter bought for £25 and sold for £18.

  Percentage loss $= \frac{7}{25} \times 100 = 28\%$

  > Percentage decrease $= \dfrac{\text{actual decrease}}{\text{initial value}} \times 100\%$
  >
  > Percentage increase $= \dfrac{\text{actual increase}}{\text{initial value}} \times 100\%$

Exercise 7

Do not use a calculator for questions 1 to 12.

1 What percentage of these rectangles are shaded?

(a) 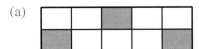 (b) 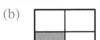 (c)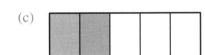

2 Write $\frac{1}{2}$, 0.02 and 20% in order of size, smallest first.

3 Work out (a) 10% of 20 pence, (b) 25% of 60 kg, (c) 5% of £900.

4 In an examination Felicity scored 75% of the marks and Daisy scored $\frac{4}{5}$ of the marks. Who has the better score? Give a reason for your answer.

5 Copy and complete this table.

Fraction	$\frac{3}{4}$		$\frac{3}{5}$
Decimal	0.75	0.3	
Percentage			

6 In a survey, 500 people were questioned about things they recycled.
25% of the people said they recycled paper. How many people is this?　　Edexcel

7 A pop concert is attended by 35 000 people. 2% of the people are given a free T-shirt.
How many people are given a free T-shirt?

8 Work out 30% of £45.

9 Andy is given £4 pocket money. He spends 15% of it on a magazine.
How much was the magazine?

10 What is (a) 60 pence as a percentage of £3, (b) 15 seconds as a percentage of 1 minute?

11 Mira earns £600 a week. She is given a pay rise of £30 a week.
What is the percentage increase in her pay?

12 Class 11A has 30 pupils. 18 of these pupils are girls.
What percentage of the class is girls?　　Edexcel

13 180 college students apply for jobs at a new supermarket.
(a) 70% of the students are given an interview.
How many students are given an interview?
(b) 54 students are offered jobs.
What percentage of the students who applied were offered jobs?

14 A phone normally costs £90. The price is reduced by 20% in a sale.
What is the price of the phone in the sale?

15 Maggie normally works Monday to Friday and is paid £6.50 per hour.
When she works on a Saturday she is paid 30% **more**.
How much is she paid per hour for working on a Saturday?

16 Harvey sees this advertisement.
Calculate the actual price of the language course.

17 Find 48% of £9.50.

18 In an experiment a spring is extended from 12 cm to 15 cm.
Calculate the percentage increase in the length of the spring.

19
Find the percentage reduction on the
Mega Ace Games System in the sale.　　Edexcel

20 You have to climb 123 steps to see the view from the top of a tower.

Harold has climbed 66 steps.
What percentage of the steps has he still got to climb?
Give your answer to the nearest whole number.

Time and Money

What you need to know

- Time can be given using either the **12-hour clock** or the **24-hour clock**.

  Eg 1   (a)   1120 is equivalent to 11.20 am.
            (b)   1645 is equivalent to 4.45 pm.

  > When using the 12-hour clock:
  >   times **before** midday are given as am,
  >   times **after** midday are given as pm.

- **Timetables** are usually given using the 24-hour clock.

  Eg 2   Some of the rail services from Manchester to Stoke are shown.

Manchester	0925	1115	1215	1415	1555
Stockport	0933	—	1223	—	1603
Stoke	1007	1155	1255	1459	1636

  > Some trains do not stop at every station. This is shown by a dash on the timetable.

  Kath catches the 1555 from Manchester to Stoke.
  (a)   How many minutes does the journey take?   (a)   41 minutes
  (b)   What is her arrival time in 12-hour clock time?   (b)   4.36 pm

- When considering a **best buy**, compare quantities by using the same units.

  Eg 3   Peanut butter is available in small or large jars.
            Small jar: 250 grams for 68 pence   Large jar: 454 grams for £1.25
            Which size is the better value for money?

            Small jar: $250 \div 68 = 3.67\ldots$ grams per penny
            Large jar: $454 \div 125 = 3.63\ldots$ grams per penny
            The small jar gives more grams per penny and is better value.

  > Compare the number of grams per penny for each size.

- **Value added tax**, or **VAT**, is a tax on some goods and services and is added to the bill.

  Eg 4   A freezer costs £180 + $17\frac{1}{2}$ % VAT.

  > $17\frac{1}{2}\% = 17.5\% = \frac{17.5}{100} = 0.175$

       (a)   How much is the VAT?   (a)   VAT = £180 × 0.175 = £31.50
       (b)   What is the total cost of the freezer?   (b)   Total cost = £180 + £31.50 = £211.50

- **Exchange rates** are used to show what £1 will buy in foreign currencies.

  Eg 5   Alex buys a painting for 80 euros in France.
            The exchange rate is 1.55 euros to the £.
            What is the cost of the painting in £s?

            1.55 euros = £1   80 euros = 80 ÷ 1.55 = £51.6129…
            The painting cost £51.61, to the nearest penny.

Exercise 8   Do not use a calculator for questions 1 to 5.

1   Tom buys the following items from a shop.

> 6 tins of baked beans at 18p each,
> 5 tins of cat food at 37p each,
> 2 packets of tea bags at £1.41 each.

(a)   Work out the total cost of these items.

Tom went into the shop at 0953.
He came out of the shop at 1002.
(b)   For how many minutes was Tom in the shop?

Edexcel

2 Here is part of a bus timetable.

Wigan, bus station	0530	0555	0620	—	0640
Hindley Green	0552	0617	0642	—	0702
Atherton	0558	0623	0648	0700	0710
Tyldesley	0604	0629	0654	0706	0716
Monton Green	0625	0650	0715	0729	0739
Eccles	0631	0656	0722	0736	0746
Trafford Road	0636	0701	0730	0744	0754

(a) At what time should the 0620 from Wigan arrive at Monton Green?
(b) How long should it take the 0629 bus from Tyldesley to travel to Trafford Road?

Susan catches a bus in Atherton. She needs to be in Eccles by 0700.
(c) What is the time of the latest bus she could catch from Atherton?

Edexcel

3 Reg travels to Ireland. The exchange rate is 1.60 euros to the £.
(a) He changes £40 into euros.
How many euros does he receive?
(b) A taxi fare costs 10 euros.
What is the cost of the taxi fare in pounds and pence?

4 The table below shows the cost of hiring a wallpaper stripper.

Cost for the first day	Extra cost per day for each additional day
£7.50	£2.50

Vivian hires the wallpaper stripper.
The total cost of hiring the wallpaper stripper was £35.
How many days did Vivian hire it for?

5 Nick is on holiday in Spain.
He hires a car at the rates shown.

There are 1.60 euros to £1.

Nick hires the car for 5 days and drives
it for a total of 720 kilometres.
Calculate the total cost of hiring the car.
Give your answer in pounds.

CAR HIRE
Daily rate — 54 euros
Free kilometres per day — 120
Excess kilometre charge — 0.60 euros

6 Toffee is sold in bars of two sizes.
A large bar weighs 450 g and costs £1.69. A small bar weighs 275 g and costs 99p.
Which size of bar is better value for money?
You must show all your working.

7 Mrs Tilsed wishes to buy a car priced at £2400.

Two options are available.
Option 1 – A deposit of 20% of £2400 and 24 monthly payments of £95.
Option 2 – For a single payment the dealer offers a discount of 5% on £2400.

How much more does it cost to buy the car if option 1 is chosen rather than option 2?

8 Sam wants to buy a Hooper washing machine.
Hooper washing machines are sold in three different shops.

Washing Power	Whytes	Clean Up
¼ OFF usual price of £330	20% OFF usual price of £320	£210 plus VAT at 17½%

Work out the cost of the washing machine in each shop.

Edexcel

Personal Finance

What you need to know

- **Hourly pay** is paid at a **basic rate** for a fixed number of hours.
  Overtime pay is usually paid at a higher rate such as time and a half, which means each hour's work is worth 1.5 times the basic rate.

  Eg 1 Alexis is paid £7.20 per hour for a basic 35-hour week.
  Overtime is paid at time and a half.
  Last week she worked 38 hours. How much was Alexis paid last week?

Basic pay	$= £7.20 \times 35$	$= £252$
Overtime pay	$= 1.5 \times £7.20 \times 3$	$= £\ 32.40$
Total pay	$= £252 + £32.40$	$= \underline{£284.40}$

- Everyone is allowed to earn some money which is not taxed. This is called a **tax allowance**.

- Tax is only paid on income earned in excess of the tax allowance. This is called **taxable income**.

  Eg 2 Tom earns £5800 per year. His tax allowance is £4615 per year and he pays tax at 10p in the £ on his taxable income. Find how much income tax Tom pays per year.

Taxable income	$= £5800 - £4615 = £1185$
Income tax payable	$= £1185 \times 0.10 = £118.50$

  > First find the taxable income, then multiply taxable income by rate in £.

- Gas, electricity and telephone bills are paid **quarterly**.
  The bill consists of a standing charge plus a charge for the amount used.

- You should be able to work out a variety of problems involving personal finance.

Exercise 9

Do not use a calculator for questions 1 to 6.

1 Jenny worked $2\frac{1}{2}$ hours at £5.20 per hour. How much did she earn?

2 Amrit pays his council tax by 10 instalments.
His first instalment is £143.25 and the other 9 instalments are £137 each.
How much is his total council tax?

3 Helen insures her house for £118 000 and its contents for £22 500.
The premiums for the insurance are:

> House: . . . . £1.30 per annum for every £1000 of cover.
> Contents: . . . . . . 24p per annum for every £100 of cover.

What is the total cost of Helen's insurance?

4 Last year Harry paid the following gas bills.

£146.32	£42.87	£36.55	£133.06

This year he will pay his gas bills by 12 equal monthly payments.
Use last year's gas bills to calculate his monthly payments.

5 Travis is paid £6.67 per hour. Last week he worked 32 hours.
By using suitable approximations estimate how much he was paid for last week.
You must show all your working.

6 Esther has an annual income of £6507. She has a tax allowance of £4615.
(a) Calculate her taxable income.

She pays tax at the rate of 10p in the £ on her taxable income.
(b) How much income tax does she pay per year?

7 Felix is paid at time and a half for overtime. His overtime rate of pay is £8.40 per hour.
What is his basic rate of pay?

8 Ivor receives his gas bill. The charge for the gas he has used is £148 plus VAT at 5%.
(a) Calculate the VAT charged.
(b) Hence, find the total amount he has to pay.

9 Angela is paid £5.40 per hour for a basic 35-hour week. Overtime is paid at time and a half.
One week Angela worked $37\frac{1}{2}$ hours. How much did Angela earn that week?

10 Ernie earns £495 per month. He has a tax allowance of £4615 per year.
He pays tax at the rate of 10p in the pound on his taxable income.
How much income tax does he pay per year?

11 The table below shows the monthly payments for an insurance scheme.
The payments depend on the age at which a person starts paying.
There are two rates, Standard Rate and Discount Rate.

Age	Monthly Payments per Person	
	Standard Rate	Discount Rate
0 - 16	£7.20	£6.12
17 - 19	£12.60	£10.71
20 - 39	£17.00	£14.45
40 - 59	£23.40	£19.89
60 - 74	£41.40	£35.19
75 and over	£84.80	£72.08

Alison is aged 17. She pays the Standard Rate.
(a) (i) Write down Alison's monthly payment.
(ii) Work out the total amount Alison will pay in a year.

Mr Masih pays the Discount Rate. He pays £19.89 each month.
If he were one year older, he would have to pay £35.19 each month.
(b) How old is Mr Masih?

The Standard monthly payment for an insurance scheme for Tom is £7.20.
This is reduced for the Discount monthly payment to £6.12.
(c) Work out the percentage reduction.

Edexcel

12 Francis is paid £4.80 per hour for a basic 35-hour week.
One week Francis also works overtime at time and a half. His total pay that week was £196.80.
How many hours overtime did he work that week?

13 Leroy earns £13 600 per year.
He has a tax allowance of £4615 and pays tax at the rate of 10p in the £ on the first £1920 of
his taxable income and 22p in the £ on the remainder.
How much income tax does he pay each year?

14 An electricity bill is made up of two parts.

A standing charge of £9.78 and
a charge of 6.36p for each unit of electricity used.

VAT at 5% is added to the total. Mr Hill has used 452 units of electricity.
Calculate his electricity bill.

Personal Finance . . . . Personal Finance . . . .

Ratio and Proportion

What you need to know

- The ratio 3 : 2 is read '3 to 2'.

- A ratio is used only to **compare** quantities.
  A ratio does not give information about the exact values of quantities being compared.

- Different forms of the **same ratio**, such as 2 : 1 and 6 : 3, are called **equivalent ratios**.

- In its **simplest form**, a ratio contains whole numbers which have no common factor other than 1.

  Eg 1 Write £2.40 : 40p in its simplest form.
  £2.40 : 40p = 240p : 40p
  $\qquad\qquad\quad$ = 240 : 40
  $\qquad\qquad\quad$ = 6 : 1

  > All quantities in a ratio must
  > be in the **same units** before the
  > ratio can be simplified.

- You should be able to solve a variety of problems involving ratio.

  Eg 2 The ratio of bats to balls in a box is 2 : 3.
  There are 12 bats in the box.
  How many balls are there?

  $12 \div 2 = 6$
  $2 \times 6 : 3 \times 6 = 12 : 18$
  There are 18 balls in the box.

  > For every 2 bats there are 3 balls.
  > To find an equivalent ratio to 2 : 3,
  > in which the first number is 12,
  > multiply each number in the ratio by 6.

  Eg 3 A wall costs £600 to build.
  The costs of materials to labour are in
  the ratio 1 : 4.
  What is the cost of labour?

  $1 + 4 = 5$
  £600 ÷ 5 = £120
  Cost of labour = £120 × 4 = £480

  > The numbers in the ratio add to 5.
  > For every £5 of the total cost, £1 pays
  > for materials and £4 pays for labour.
  > So, **divide** by 5 and then **multiply** by 4.

- When two different quantities are always in the **same ratio** the two quantities are in
  direct proportion.

  Eg 4 20 litres of petrol cost £14.
  Find the cost of 25 litres of petrol.

  20 litres cost £14
  1 litre costs £14 ÷ 20 = £0.70
  25 litres cost £0.70 × 25 = £17.50

  > This is sometimes called the **unitary method**.
  > **Divide** by 20 to find the cost of 1 litre.
  > **Multiply** by 25 to find the cost of 25 litres.

Exercise 10

Do not use a calculator for questions 1 to 6.

1 Write these ratios in their simplest form.
   (a) 2 : 6 $\quad$ (b) 8 : 4 $\quad$ (c) 6 : 9

2 Rhys draws a plan of his classroom floor. The classroom measures 15 m by 20 m.
   He draws the plan to a scale of 1 cm to 5 m.
   What are the measurements of the classroom floor on the plan?

3 A toy box contains large bricks and small bricks in the ratio 1 : 4.
   The box contains 40 bricks. How many large bricks are in the box?

4 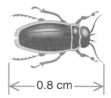 This magnifying glass makes things look bigger.
It enlarges in the ratio 1 : 5.
What is the length of the beetle under the magnifying glass?

Not to scale ←—0.8 cm—→

5 To make mortar a builder mixes sand and cement in the ratio 3 : 1.
The builder uses 2.5 kg of cement. How much sand does he use?

6 Stephen and Joanne share £210 in the radio 6 : 1.
How much more money does Stephen get than Joanne?

Edexcel

7 In a drama club the ratio of boys to girls is 1 : 3.
(a) What fraction of the club members are boys?
(b) What percentage of the club members are girls?

8 Robert used these ingredients to make 24 buns.

> 100 g of butter, 80 g of sugar, 90 g of flour,
> 2 eggs, 30 ml of milk

Robert wants to make 36 similar buns.
Write down how much of each ingredient he
needs for 36 buns.

Edexcel

9 The ratio of men to women playing golf one day is 7 : 3.
(a) What percentage of the people playing golf are men?
(b) There are 21 men playing. How many women are playing?

10  Three 1-litre tins of paint cost a total of £26.85.
Find the cost of five of the 1-litre tins of paint.

Edexcel

11 Two students are talking about their school outing.

> My class went to Tower Bridge last week.
> There are 30 people in my class.
> The total cost was £82.50

> There are 45 people in my group.
> What will be the total cost for my group?

12 A pop concert is attended by 2100 people.
The ratio of males to females is 2 : 3.
How many males attended the concert?

13 Rashid has 35 sweets.
He shares them in the ratio 4 : 3 with his sister.
Rashid keeps the larger share.
How many sweets does Rashid keep?

Edexcel

14 Naheed is given £4. She spends £3.20 and saves the rest.
Express the amount she spends to the amount she saves as a ratio in its simplest form.

15 On a map the distance between two towns is 5 cm.
The actual distance between the towns is 1 kilometre.
What is the scale of the map in the form of 1 : n?

Ratio and Proportion

Section Review - Number

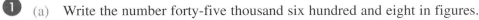

Do not use a calculator for questions 1 to 32.

1 (a) Write the number forty-five thousand six hundred and eight in figures.
(b) Write your answer to part (a) to the nearest thousand.   Edexcel

2 (a) (i) Write these numbers in order of size, smallest first: 16   10   6   100   61
(ii) What is the total when the numbers are added together?
(b) Work out.   (i) $100 - 37$ (ii) 100×20 (iii) $100 \div 4$

3 $\frac{3}{4}$ of this shape is shaded.
(a) What percentage of the shape is shaded?
(b) What percentage of the shape is **not** shaded?   Edexcel

4 Orange juice is sold in cartons of two different sizes.

(a) How much is saved by buying a 500 ml carton instead of two 250 ml cartons?

(b) Reg buys four 500 ml cartons.
He pays with a £5 note.
How much change is he given?

5 The distance from London to Edinburgh via Newcastle is 600 km.
Newcastle is 176 km from Edinburgh.
How far is it from London to Newcastle?

6 An overnight train leaves Dundee at 2348 and arrives in London at 0735 the next day.
How long does the journey take?
Give your answer in hours and minutes.

7 Work out $40 \times 50 \times 500$.   Give your answer in words.

8 Use the numbers in the cloud to answer these questions.
(a) Which numbers are even numbers?
(b) Which numbers are multiples of 3?
(c) Which numbers are the square roots of another number in the cloud?   Edexcel

9 (a) 4 litres of milk costs £1.96. How much is 1 litre of milk?
(b) Apples cost 84 pence per kilogram. What is the cost of 5 kilograms of apples?

10 To buy a car, Ricky has to pay 24 monthly payments of £198.
How much does he have to pay altogether to buy the car?

11 Write these numbers in order of size.
Start with the largest number.

| 0.8 | 70% | $\frac{7}{8}$ | $\frac{3}{4}$ |

Edexcel

12 A ski-run measures 7.5 cm on a map. The map is drawn to a scale of 1 cm to 200 m.
What is the actual length of the ski-run in metres?

13 247 pupils and 13 teachers are going on a school visit by coach.
Each coach holds 55 passengers.
(a) How many coaches are needed?

Each coach costs £157.50 to hire.
(b) How much will the coaches cost altogether?   Edexcel

14

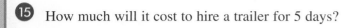

3,   6,   8,   9,   15,   24,   28,   43,   48,   64

Write down two numbers from the list above which
(a)   are **both** multiples of 12,   (b)   are **both** factors of 12,
(c)   are **both** square numbers,   (d)   are **both** cube numbers.

Edexcel

15   How much will it cost to hire a trailer for 5 days?

TRAILERS FOR HIRE

£3.50 per day
plus £12.50 insurance

16   (a)   Write 0.8 as a fraction.
(b)   Write 57.419 correct to   (i)   1 decimal place,   (ii)   2 decimal places.
(c)   Find the square of 7.

17   A sports club is given £100 to spend on new footballs. A new football costs £7.99.
What is the greatest number of footballs they can buy?

18   (a)   Calculate the cost per litre of emulsion paint,
correct to the nearest penny.

(b)   How much more does it cost to buy
10 litres of gloss paint than
10 litres of emulsion paint?

GLOSS
PAINT
5 litres

EMULSION
PAINT
10 litres

£12.95

£14.99

19   In a long jump event Hanniah jumped the following distances.
5.15 m   4.95 m   5.20 m   5.02 m   5.10 m
(a)   Write down the shortest distance Hanniah jumped.
(b)   Write these distances in order, shortest first.

20   Javaid took part in a sponsored slim.
His starting weight was 73 kg.
The table shows the number of kilograms he
gained or lost each week.
How much did Javaid weigh at the end of 4 weeks?

Week 1	−2 kg
Week 2	+1 kg
Week 3	−3 kg
Week 4	−1 kg

21   A crowd of 54 000 people watch a carnival.
(a)   15% of the crowd are men. How many men watch the carnival?
(b)   Two-thirds of the crowd are children. How many children watch the carnival?

22   Sonia is paid a basic rate of £4.80 per hour for working a 30-hour week from Monday to Friday.
(a)   How much is Sonia paid each week?

When Sonia works on a Saturday she is paid at time and a half.
(b)   How much is Sonia paid for 1 hour's work on a Saturday?
(c)   For working last Saturday Sonia was paid £21.60.
How many hours did she work last Saturday?

23   Find $\frac{3}{4}$ of £28.

24   (a)   (i)   What is the value of the 3 in the number 2439?
(ii)   What is the value of the 3 in the answer to 2439 × 100?
(b)   Work out   (i)   8 − 3 × 2,   (ii)   15 ÷ (3 + 2) − 1.
(c)   Work out   (i)   137 × 32,   (ii)   432 ÷ 12.

25   (a)   Write down two numbers you could use to estimate the answer to   793 ÷ 21.
(b)   Work out your estimate.

Edexcel

26 Some of the rail services from Poole to Waterloo are shown.

Poole	0544	0602	—	0640	—	0740	0825	0846
Bournemouth	0558	0616	—	0654	0715	0754	0839	0900
Southampton	0634	0655	0714	0738	0754	0838	0908	0938
Eastleigh	0646	—	—	0750	—	0852	—	0951
Waterloo	0804	0810	0844	0901	0908	1005	1018	1112

(a) Sid arrives at Bournemouth station at 0830.
What is the time of the next train to Eastleigh?

(b) Paul catches the 0654 from Bournemouth to Southampton.
How many minutes does the journey take?

27 Calculate. (a) 256×37 (b) $925 \div 37$ Edexcel

28 The lowest temperatures recorded in Manchester each night for a week are given.

$$7°C, \quad -4°C, \quad 3°C, \quad 1°C, \quad -2°C, \quad 0°C, \quad -1°C$$

(a) Write down the temperatures in order. Start with the lowest temperature.

(b) Work out the difference between the highest and lowest temperatures.   Edexcel

29 (a) Write these decimals in order, from smallest to largest.

$$0.345 \quad 0.35 \quad -0.4 \quad 0.355 \quad -0.35$$

(b) Write down a decimal that lies halfway between 0.4 and 0.5.

(c) Work out. (i) $5 - 0.26$ (ii) 0.2×0.4 (iii) $24 \div 0.3$

(d) A turkey costs £2.40 per kilogram.
What is the cost of a turkey which weighs 6.5 kilograms?

30 (a) Work out (i) 10^5,   (ii) $10^2 - 2^3$,   (iii) $2^3 \times 3^2$,   (iv) $30^2 \div 10^3$.

(b) Which is smaller, 5^2 or 3^3? Show **all** your working.

(c) Work out $\sqrt{16} \times \sqrt{100}$.

31 Members of the Art Club at Oldcastle School wish to hire a coach for a day trip to London and back.
There are two possible firms to hire from, Northlands and Eastline.
The total cost to hire the coach from Northlands is £562.80, which consists of a fixed charge of £100 and a charge of 52p per kilometre.

(a) (i) How many kilometres is the journey to London and back?

(ii) Given that 1 kilometre is 0.62 miles, change your answer into miles.

Eastline charge £1 per mile and make no fixed charge.

(b) Calculate the **saving** which the club would make by hiring from Eastline instead of Northlands?   Edexcel

32 (a) Write these fractions in ascending order: $\frac{1}{2}$ $\frac{2}{3}$ $\frac{3}{5}$ $\frac{5}{8}$ $\frac{3}{4}$

(b) Write down a fraction that lies halfway between $\frac{1}{5}$ and $\frac{1}{4}$.

(c) Work out. (i) $\frac{1}{4} + \frac{2}{5}$ (ii) $\frac{2}{3} - \frac{1}{2}$ (iii) $\frac{4}{5} \times \frac{1}{2}$

(d) Work out $\frac{2}{5}$ of 12.

33 (a) Write $\frac{13}{20}$ as a decimal.

(b) In a spelling test Lara scores 13 out of 20. What is Lara's score as a percentage?

34 (a) Given that $576 \times 135 = 77\,760$, find: (i) 57.6×13.5 (ii) $\dfrac{7776}{5760}$

(b) Write 77 760 correct to one significant figure.

35

A jacket is 70% wool and 30% nylon.

(a) Write 70% as a decimal.

(b) Write 30% as a fraction.
Give your answer in its simplest form.

(c) Write down the ratio of wool to nylon.

Edexcel

36 Bertie has to work out $4.2 \times 4.9 \times 31$.   He uses a calculator and gets   6379.8

(a) By rounding each number to one significant figure check Bertie's answer.
Show all your working.

(b) What is the mistake in Bertie's answer?

37 Pepe travels from Spain to the USA for a holiday.
He changes 2000 euros into dollars.
Calculate how many dollars he will get.
Give your answer to the nearest dollar.

> **TOURIST RATES**
> *£1 will buy*
> Spain . . . . . . 1.64 euros
> USA . . . . . . 1.48 dollars

38 Two lettuces and three cucumbers cost £2.67.
Cucumbers cost 59p each.
How much does a lettuce cost?

39

Frances sees three different advertisements for jeans.
Work out the cost of the jeans in each advertisement.

Edexcel

40 To make squash, orange juice and water is mixed in the ratio of 1 : 6.
How much orange juice is needed to make 35 litres of squash?

41 Mrs Joy's electricity meter was read on 1st March and 1st June.

On 1st March the reading was | 3 | 2 | 4 | 5 | 7 | On 1st June the reading was | 3 | 2 | 9 | 3 | 1 |

(a) How many units of electricity have been used?

Her electricity bill for this period includes a fixed charge of £9.58 and the cost of the units
used at 6.36 pence per unit.

(b) Calculate the total cost of electricity for this period.

42 In England, a jar of **extra fruity** apricot jam weighs 454 g and costs 89p.
In France, a jar of **extra fruity** apricot jam weighs 681 g and costs 1.84 euros.
   £1 = 1.58 euros.
In which country is the jam better value for money?
You must show all your working.

43 Evaluate $\dfrac{(23.4 + 35.6) \times 5.7}{200.3 \times (16.2 - 8.15)}$

Edexcel

44 (a) What is the reciprocal of 0.25?   (b) Calculate $2.5^2 + \dfrac{1}{2.5}$.

45 A caravan is for sale at £7200. Stuart buys the caravan on credit.

The credit terms are: deposit 25% of sale price and 36 monthly payments of £175.

Express the extra amount paid for credit, compared with the cash price,
as a percentage of the cash price.

Introduction to Algebra

What you need to know

- You should be able to write **algebraic expressions**.

  Eg 1 An expression for the cost of 6 pens at n pence each is $6n$ pence.

- Be able to **simplify expressions** by collecting **like terms** together.

  Eg 2 (a) $2d + 3d = 5d$ (b) $3x + 2 - x + 4 = 2x + 6$ (c) $x + 2x + x^2 = 3x + x^2$

- Be able to **multiply expressions** together.

  Eg 3 (a) $2 \times a \times a = 2a^2$ (b) $y \times y \times y = y^3$ (c) $m \times 3n = 3mn$

- Be able to **multiply out brackets**.

  Eg 4 (a) $2(x + 5) = 2x + 10$ (b) $x(x - 5) = x^2 - 5x$

- Be able to **factorise expressions**.

  Eg 5 (a) $3x - 6 = 3(x - 2)$ (b) $m^2 + 5m = m(m + 5)$

Exercise 11

1 A calculator costs £9. Write an expression for the cost of k calculators.

2 Godfrey is 5 years older than Mary.
Write an expression for Godfrey's age when Mary is t years old.

3 A cup of coffee costs x pence and a cup of tea costs y pence.
Write an expression for the cost of 3 cups of coffee and 2 cups of tea.

4 Write an expression, in terms of x,
for the sum of the angles in this shape.

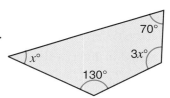

5 A muffin costs $d + 3$ pence. Write an expression for the cost of 5 muffins.

6 Simplify   (a) $5x + 3x - x$,   (b) $4y - 3 + 3y - 2$.   Edexcel

7 Which algebraic expressions are equivalent?

$a + a$	$2(a + 1)$	$2a + 1$	$2a + 2$	a^3
a^2	$a + a + 1$	$2a$	$a + a + a$	$a \times a$

8 (a) Simplify   (i) $2x + 3 + x$,   (ii) $2x + y - x + y$.
(b) Multiply out   (i) $2(x + 3)$,   (ii) $x(x - 1)$.
(c) Multiply out and simplify   (i) $2(x - 1) - 3$,   (ii) $7 + 3(2 + x)$.
(d) Factorise   (i) $2a - 6$,   (ii) $x^2 + 2x$.

9 (a) Simplify. (i) $x + x + x$ (ii) $2a + 4b + a - 2b$ (iii) $3(a + 2)$
(b) Expand and simplify. $2(x - 1) + 3(2x + 1)$ Edexcel

Solving Equations ●●●●●●●●

What you need to know

- The solution of an equation is the value of the unknown letter that fits the equation.
- You should be able to solve simple equations by **inspection**.

  Eg 1 (a) $a + 2 = 5$ (b) $m - 3 = 7$ (c) $2x = 10$

  $\quad\quad\quad\quad a = 3$ $\quad\quad\quad\quad m = 10$ $\quad\quad\quad\quad x = 5$

- Be able to solve simple problems by **working backwards**.

  Eg 2 I think of a number, multiply it by 3 and add 4. The answer is 19.

The number I thought of is 5.

- Be able to use the **balance method** to solve equations.

  Eg 3 Solve these equations.

  (a) $d - 13 = -5$ (b) $-4a = 20$ (c) $5 - 4n = -1$

  $\quad\quad d = -5 + 13$ $\quad\quad a = \frac{20}{-4}$ $\quad\quad -4n = -6$

  $\quad\quad d = 8$ $\quad\quad a = -5$ $\quad\quad n = 1.5$

Exercise 12

1 What number should be put in the box to make each of these statements correct?

(a) $\boxed{} - 6 = 9$ (b) $2 + \boxed{} = 11$ (c) $4 \times \boxed{} = 20$ (d) $\boxed{} \times 3 - 5 = 7$

2 Solve these equations.

(a) $7 + x = 12$ (b) $5 - x = 3$ (c) $3x = 21$ (d) $2x - 1 = 5$

3 Lindi thought of a number. She multiplied the number by 5. Her answer was 30.
What number did Lindi think of?

Edexcel

4 The diagram shows a mathematical rule.
Copy and complete the table.

Input	3		−2
Output		13	

5 (a) I think of a number, add 3, and then multiply by 2.
The answer is 16. What is my number?
(b) I think of a number, double it and then subtract 3.
The answer is 5. What is my number?

6 Solve these equations.

(a) $3x - 7 = 23$ (b) $4 + 3x = 19$ (c) $5x - 9 = 11$ (d) $5 - 7x = 47$

7 Solve these equations.

(a) $3x + 5 = 2$ (b) $4x = 2$ (c) $4x + 1 = 23$ (d) $5x + 1 = -3$

What you need to know

- To solve an equation you need to find the numerical value of the letter, by ending up with **one letter** on one side of the equation and a **number** on the other side of the equation.

- You should be able to solve equations with unknowns on both sides of the equals sign.

  Eg 1 Solve $3x + 1 = x + 7$.

  $$3x = x + 6$$
  $$2x = 6$$
  $$x = 3$$

- Be able to solve equations which include brackets.

  Eg 2 Solve $2(x - 3) = 4$.

  $$2x - 6 = 4$$
  $$2x = 10$$
  $$x = 5$$

- You should be able to write, or form, equations using the information given in a problem.

Exercise 13

1 Solve the equations (a) $3x - 7 = x + 15$, (b) $5(x - 2) = 20$.

2 Solve these equations.
(a) $7x + 4 = 60$ (b) $3x - 7 = -4$ (c) $2(x + 3) = -2$ (d) $3x - 4 = 1 + x$

3 Solve the equations (a) $2p - 3 = 7$, (b) $6 - q = 7$, (c) $3r - 4 = 7r + 2$.
Edexcel

4 Solve these equations.
(a) $2x + 5 = 2$ (b) $2(x - 1) = 3$ (c) $5 - 2x = 3x + 2$ (d) $2(3 + x) = 9$

5 Solve. (a) $5t - 1 = 24$ (b) $4x + 3 = 2x + 10$ (c) $7y + 21 = 3y - 3$ Edexcel

6 The lengths of these rods are given, in centimetres, in terms of n.

 n 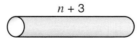 $n + 3$ $2n - 1$

(a) Write an expression, in terms of n, for the total length of the rods.
(b) The total length of the rods is 30 cm.
By forming an equation, find the value of n.

7 Mandy buys a small box of chocolates and a large box of chocolates.
The diagram shows the number of chocolates in each box.

n $2n + 5$
chocolates   chocolates

Altogether there are 47 chocolates.
By forming an equation, find the number of chocolates in the larger box.

8 Solve the equation $5(x - 3) = 2x$.

Formulae

What you need to know

- An **expression** is just an answer using letters and numbers.
  A **formula** is an algebraic rule. It always has an equals sign.

- You should be able to **write simple formulae**.

  Eg 1 A packet of crisps weighs 25 grams.
  Write a formula for the total weight,
  W grams, of n packets of crisps.
  $$W = 25n$$

  Eg 2 Start with t, add 5 and then multiply
  by 3. The result is p.
  Write a formula for p in terms of t.
  $$p = 3(t + 5)$$

- Be able to **substitute** values into given expressions and formulae.

  Eg 3
  (a) Find the value
  of $4x - y$ when
  $x = 5$ and $y = 7$.
  $$\begin{aligned} 4x - y &= 4 \times 5 - 7 \\ &= 20 - 7 \\ &= 13 \end{aligned}$$

  (b) $A = pq - r$
  Find the value
  of A when $p = 2$,
  $q = -2$ and $r = 3$.
  $$\begin{aligned} A &= pq - r \\ &= 2 \times (-2) - 3 \\ &= -4 - 3 \\ &= -7 \end{aligned}$$

  (c) $M = 2n^2$
  Find the value
  of M when $n = 3$.
  $$\begin{aligned} M &= 2n^2 \\ &= 2 \times 3^2 \\ &= 2 \times 9 \\ &= 18 \end{aligned}$$

Exercise 14

Do not use a calculator for questions 1 to 8.

1 What is the value of $a - 3b$ when $a = 10$ and $b = 2$?

2 What is the value of $2x + y$ when $x = -3$ and $y = 5$?

3 $P = 2l + 2w$. $l = 12$ and $w = 8$. Work out the value of P. *Edexcel*

4 $H = ab - c$. Find the value of H when $a = 2$, $b = -5$ and $c = 3$.

5 A pie costs 65 pence. Pam buys n pies. The total cost is C pence.
Write down a formula connecting C and n. *Edexcel*

6 $L = 5(p + q)$. Find the value of L when $p = 2$ and $q = -4$.

7 $A = b - cd$. Find the value of A when $b = -3$, $c = 2$ and $d = 4$.

8 What is the value of $10y^2$ when $y = 3$?

9 The cost of using an appliance is calculated by the formula:

> **cost = number of kilowatts × number of hours × 7 pence**

Find the cost of using (a) a 3 kilowatt heater for 5 hours,
(b) a 0.36 kilowatt TV set for 50 hours. *Edexcel*

10 This rule is used to change miles into kilometres.

> Multiply the number of miles by 8 and then divide by 5

(a) Use the rule to change 25 miles into kilometres.
(b) Using K for the number of kilometres and M for the number of miles
write a formula for K in terms of M.
(c) Use your formula to find the value of M when $K = 60$.

What you need to know

- A **sequence** is a list of numbers made according to some rule.
  The numbers in a sequence are called **terms**.

- You should be able to draw and continue number sequences represented by patterns of shapes.

  Eg 1 This pattern represents the sequence:
  3, 5, 7, …

- Be able to continue a sequence by following a given rule.

  Eg 2 The sequence 2, 7, 22, … is made using the rule:

  > Multiply the last number by 3, then add 1.

  The next term in the sequence $= (22 \times 3) + 1 = 66 + 1 = 67$

- Be able to find a rule, and then use it, to continue a sequence.

  > **To continue a sequence:**
  > 1. Work out the rule to get from one term to the next.
  > 2. Apply the same rule to find further terms in the sequence.

  Eg 3 Describe the rule used to make the following sequences.
  Then use the rule to find the next term of each sequence.

  (a) 5, 8, 11, 14, …   (b) 2, 4, 8, 16, …   (c) 1, 1, 2, 3, 5, 8, …
  Rule: Rule: Rule:
  add 3 to last term   multiply last term by 2   add the last two terms
  Next term: 17   Next term: 32   Next term: 13

  > **Special sequences - Square numbers:**   1, 4, 9, 16, 25, …
  > **Triangular numbers:** 1, 3, 6, 10, 15, …

Exercise 15

1 Write down the next two terms in each of these sequences.
  (a) 1, 5, 9, 13, 17, …   (b) 50, 46, 42, 38, 34, …

2 The diagrams show patterns made out of sticks.

         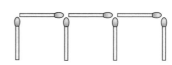

Pattern number1   **Pattern number 2**   **Pattern number 3**

(a) Draw a diagram to show pattern number 4.

The table can be used to show the
number of sticks needed for a pattern.
(b) Copy and complete the table.

Pattern number	1	2	3	4	5	6	7
Number of sticks	3	5					

(c) (i) Work out the number of sticks needed for pattern number 15.
  (ii) Explain how you obtained your answer.

Edexcel

28

3 The first three patterns in a sequence are shown.

  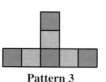

Pattern 1   **Pattern 2**   **Pattern 3**

(a) Draw Pattern 4.
(b) How many squares are in Pattern 5?
    Explain how you found your answer.
(c) There are 58 squares in Pattern 20.
    How many squares are in Pattern 19?

4 What is the next number in each of these sequences?
(a) 1, 2, 5, 10, ...   (b) 1, 3, 9, 27, ...   (c) 1, $\frac{1}{2}$, $\frac{1}{4}$, $\frac{1}{8}$, ...

5 Here are the first four terms in a sequence: 6, 12, 18, 24.
(a) (i) Write down the 5th term in the sequence.
    (ii) Explain how you worked out your answer.
(b) Which term in the sequence is equal to 72?

Edexcel

6 Look at this sequence of numbers. 2, 5, 8, 11, ...
(a) What is the next number in the sequence?
(b) Is 30 a number in this sequence?
    Give a reason for your answer.

7 The rule for a sequence is:

Add the last two numbers and divide by 2.

Write down the next three terms when the sequence begins: 3, 7, ...

8 A sequence begins: 5, 15, 45, 135, ...
(a) Write down the rule, in words, used to get from one term to the next in the sequence.
(b) Use your rule to find the next term in the sequence.

9 Here are some patterns made out of tiles.

Pattern number 1   **Pattern number 2**   **Pattern number 3**

(a) Draw pattern number 4 and pattern number 5.
(b) Copy and complete the table.

Pattern number	1	2	3	4	5	6	7
Number of tiles	1	3	6				

(c) (i) How many tiles are needed for pattern number 12?
    (ii) Explain how you found this answer.

Edexcel

10 The first six terms of a sequence are shown. 1, 4, 5, 9, 14, 23, ...
Write down the next two terms.

11 A sequence begins: 1, 6, 10, 8, ...
The rule to continue the sequence is:
double the difference between the last two numbers.
Ravi says if you continue the sequence it will end in 0. Is he correct?
Explain your answer.

12 (a) Write down the first **three** terms of the sequence whose nth term is given by $n^2 - 4$.
(b) Will the number 60 be in this sequence? Explain your answer.

Coordinates and Graphs

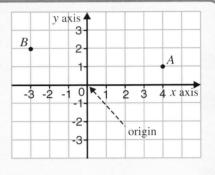

What you need to know

- **Coordinates** (involving positive and negative numbers) are used to describe the position of a point on a graph.

  | Eg 1 | The coordinates of A are $(4, 1)$.
  The coordinates of B are $(-3, 2)$.

- The x axis is the line $y = 0$. The y axis is the line $x = 0$.

- The x axis crosses the y axis at the **origin**.

- You should be able to draw the graph of a straight line.

  | Eg 2 | Draw the graphs of the following lines.

  (a) $y = 2$ (b) $x = 3$ (c) $2y = x + 2$

The graph is a **horizontal** line. All points on the line have y coordinate 2.	The graph is a **vertical** line. All points on the line have x coordinate 3.	Find values for x and y.

x	0	2	4
y	1	2	3

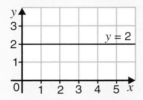 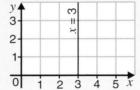 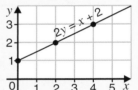

- Be able to draw the graph of a straight line by finding the points where the line crosses the x axis and the y axis.

  | Eg 3 | Draw the graph of the line $x + 2y = 4$.

To find the x coordinate of the point where a line crosses the x axis, substitute $y = 0$ into the equation of the line.

  When $y = 0$, $x + 0 = 4$, $x = 4$. Plot $(4, 0)$.

To find the y coordinate of the point where a line crosses the y axis, substitute $x = 0$ into the equation of the line.

  When $x = 0$, $0 + 2y = 4$, $y = 2$. Plot $(0, 2)$.

  A straight line drawn through the points $(0, 2)$ and $(4, 0)$ is the graph of $x + 2y = 4$.

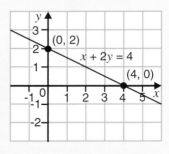

Exercise 16

1 The line joining points P and Q is shown.

(a) Write down the coordinates of points P and Q.

(b) Find the coordinates of the midpoint of the line PQ.

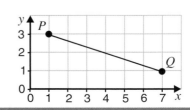

2 Points R and S are shown.

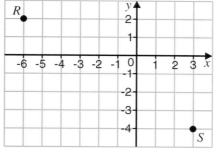

(a) Write down the coordinates of points R and S.
(b) The straight line joining R and S crosses the x axis at T.
Write down the coordinates of T.

3 Draw and label x and y axes from -5 to 4.
(a) On your diagram plot $A(4, 3)$ and $B(-5, -3)$.
(b) $C(p, -1)$ is on the line segment AB.
What is the value of p?

4 (a) On the same diagram draw the lines $y = 2$ and $x = 5$.
(b) Write down the coordinates of the point where the lines cross.

5 Write down the equations of the lines drawn on these diagrams.

(a)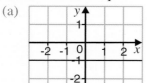

(b)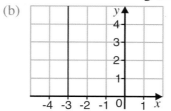

(c)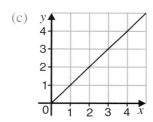

6 (a) Copy and complete the table of values for $y = 3x - 2$.

x	-1	0	1	2	3
$y = 3x - 2$					

(b) Plot your values for x and y. Join your points with a straight line.
(c) Write down the coordinates of the point where your graph crosses the y axis.   Edexcel

7 On separate diagrams draw the graphs of each of these equations for values of x from -2 to 2.
(a) $y = 2x$ (b) $y - x = 2$ (c) $y + x = 2$ (d) $2y = x$

8 On the same grid draw the graphs of   (a) $y = \frac{1}{2}x + 1$,   (b) $x = -2$.   Edexcel

9 (a) Copy and complete the table of values for $2y = 3x - 6$.

x	-2	0	4
y		-3	

(b) Draw the graph of $2y = 3x - 6$ for values of x from -2 to 4.
(c) Use your graph to find the value of x when $y = 1.5$.

10 (a) Copy and complete the table of values for the equation $5y - 2x = 10$.

x	0		5
y		0	

(b) Draw the graph of $5y - 2x = 10$ for values of x from -5 to 5.
Label the x axis from -5 to 5 and the y axis from 0 to 4.
(c) Use your graph to find the value of y when $x = -2$.

What you need to know

- A graph used to change from one quantity into an equivalent quantity is called a **conversion graph**.

  Eg 1 Use 15 kilograms = 33 pounds (lb) to draw a conversion graph for kilograms and pounds.

  Use your graph to find (a) 5 kilograms in pounds, (b) 20 pounds in kilograms.

The straight line drawn through the points (0, 0) and (33, 15) is the conversion graph for kilograms and pounds.

  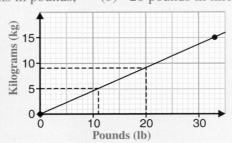

  Reading from the graph:
  (a) 5 kg = 11 lb
  (b) 20 lb = 9 kg

- **Distance-time graphs** are used to illustrate journeys.

  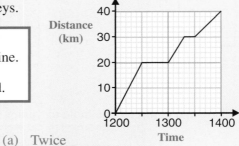

On a distance-time graph:
Speed can be calculated from the gradient of a line.
The faster the speed the steeper the gradient.
Zero gradient (horizontal line) means zero speed.

  Eg 2 The graph shows a car journey.
  (a) How many times does the car stop?   (a) Twice
  (b) (i) Between what times does the   (b) (i) 1200 to 1230.
        car travel fastest?   Steepest gradient.
        Explain your answer.
      (ii) What is the speed of the car   (ii) Speed = $\dfrac{\text{Distance}}{\text{Time}}$ = $\dfrac{20 \text{ km}}{\frac{1}{2} \text{ hour}}$ = 40 km/h
           during this part of the journey?

- You should be able to draw and interpret graphs arising from real-life situations.

Exercise **17**

1 This conversion graph can be used to convert between miles and kilometres.

  (a) Convert 50 km to miles.

  (b) Convert 27 miles to kilometres.

  (c) Explain how the information on the graph could be used to convert 10 000 km to miles.

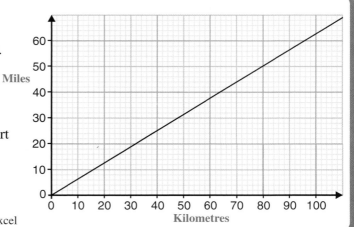

Edexcel

32

2 Ken and Wendy go from home to their caravan site.
The caravan site is 50 km from their home.
Ken goes on his bike. Wendy drives in her car.
The diagram shows information about the journeys they made.

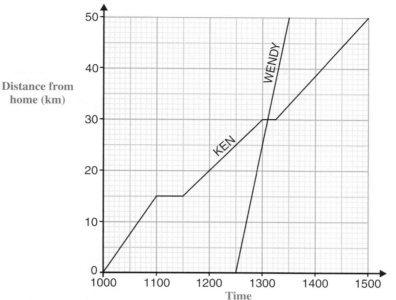

(a) At what time did Wendy pass Ken?
(b) Between which two times was Ken cycling at his greatest speed?
(c) Work out Wendy's average speed for her journey.

Edexcel

3 Reg drives from his home to the city centre.
The graph represents his journey.

(a) How long did Reg take to reach the city centre?

(b) How far from the city centre does Reg live?

(c) What is his average speed for the journey in kilometres per hour?

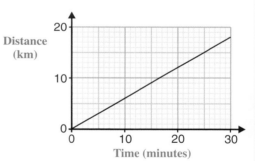

4 (a) Given that 7.4 square metres = 80 square feet,
draw a conversion graph for square metres to square feet.

(b) Use your graph to change
(i) 5 square metres into square feet,
(ii) 32 square feet into square metres.

5 The graph shows the temperature of the water in a tank as it is being heated.

(a) What was the temperature of the water before it was heated?

(b) How long did it take for the water to reach 26°C?

(c) Estimate the number of minutes it will take for the temperature of the water to rise from 32°C to 50°C.

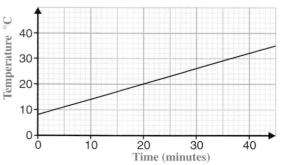

Section Review - Algebra

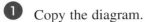

1 Copy the diagram.
   (a) Write down the coordinates of the point A.

   B is the point with coordinates (4, 3).
   (b) Mark with a cross the position of B on your grid.

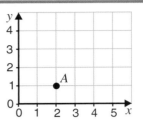

Edexcel

2 A sequence begins 2, 4, 6, …
   To continue the sequence use the rule: | Add 2 to the last term. |

   (a) Write down the next term in the sequence.
   (b) Explain why the number 99 is not a term in this sequence.

3 In each part, find the output when the input is 12.
   (a)
   Input ⟶ | × 4 | ⟶ Output

   (b)
   Input ⟶ | − 5 | ⟶ Output

4 Use this rule to find the number of points a football team has scored.

   | Points scored = 3 × Number of wins + Number of draws |

   A team wins 7 games and draws 5. How many points have they scored?

5 Regular pentagons are used to form patterns, as shown.

   Pattern 1   **Pattern 2**   **Pattern 3**

   (a) Draw Pattern 4.
   (b) Copy and complete the table.
   (c) How many sides has Pattern 5?
   (d) Pattern 10 has 32 sides.
       How many sides has Pattern 11?

Pattern number	1	2	3	4
Number of sides	5	8	11	

6 Find the value of $3a + 2b$ when $a = 5$ and $b = 3$.

7 Cheryl was working out the cost of hiring a van for a day.
   First of all she worked out the mileage cost.
   She used the formula:

   | Mileage cost = Mileage rate × Number of miles travelled |

   The mileage rate was 8 pence per mile. Cheryl travelled 240 miles.
   (a) Work out the mileage cost.

   Cheryl worked out the total hire cost by using the formula:

   | Total hire cost = Basic hire cost + Mileage cost |

   The basic hire cost was £35.
   (b) Work out the total hire cost.

   Edexcel

8 (a) A sequence begins: 1, 2, 4, 7, 11, 16, …
       (i) What is the next term in the sequence?
       (ii) Describe the rule you used to find the next term.

   (b) Another sequence uses this rule: | Add 3 to the last term. |

       What term comes before 15 in this sequence?

9 (a) A ball costs x pence. How much will 3 balls cost?
   (b) A skipping rope costs 30 pence more than a ball. How much does a skipping rope cost?

10 (a) On graph paper, plot the points $A(-3, -2)$ and $B(1, 4)$.
(b) What are the coordinates of the midpoint of AB?

11 A jam doughnut costs t pence.
(a) Write an expression for the cost of 5 jam doughnuts.

A cream doughnut costs 5 pence more than a jam doughnut.
(b) Write an expression for the cost of a cream doughnut.

12 Solve (a) $x - 3 = 7$, (b) $3x = 6$, (c) $5x + 4 = 19$.

13 Ian thought of a number.
He doubled his number and added 5. His answer was 19.
What number did Ian think of?   Edexcel

14 (a) (i) What is the next term in this sequence? 2, 9, 16, 23, …
(ii) Will the 50th term in the sequence be an odd number or an even number?
Give a reason for your answer.
(b) Another sequence begins: 1, 5, 9, 13, 17, …
Describe in words the rule for continuing the sequence.

15 $2n$ represents any even number.
Which of the statements describes the number (a) n, (b) $2n + 1$?
always even   **always odd**   **could be even or odd**

16 Simplify (a) $7x - 5x + 3x$, (b) $a - 3b + 2a - b$, (c) $3 \times m \times m$.

17 Here is a formula for working out the perimeter of a rectangle $P = 2(l + w)$.
Use the formula to work out the value of P when $l = 6$ and $w = 4$.   Edexcel

18 (a) Pablo has £t. He spends £3. How much has he got left?
(b) Cynthia has x five pound notes and $2x$ ten pound notes.
Write an expression, in terms of x, for the total value of her notes.

19 This conversion graph can be used to
change euros to dollars.

(a) Use the graph to find
(i) 20 euros in dollars,
(ii) 30 dollars in euros.

(b) Explain how you can use the graph
to change 100 euros into dollars.

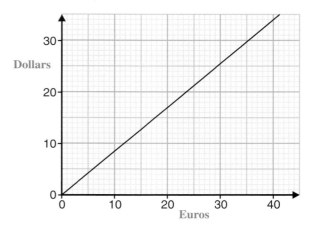

20 Powder can be mixed with water to make a milk drink.

This rule is used: | Number of spoonfuls = Amount of water (ml) ÷ 30 |

A glass contains 180 ml of water.
(a) How many spoonfuls are needed?

There are 20 spoonfuls of powder in a jug.
(b) How much water is needed?   Edexcel

21 A large envelope costs x pence and a small envelope costs y pence.
Write an expression for the cost of 3 large envelopes and 5 small envelopes.

22 (a) Copy and complete this table of values for $y = 3x - 1$.

x	-3	-2	-1	0	1	2	3
$y = 3x - 1$	-10		-4			5	

(b) Draw the graph of $y = 3x - 1$.
(c) Use your graph to find the value of x when $y = 6.5$ Edexcel

23 Which of these algebraic expressions are equivalent?

$2a - a$	$3a$	$2(a - 1)$	$2a + a$
$2a + 1$	$2a - 2$	$a + a - 1$	2

24 Solve these equations.
(a) $g - 5 = 3$ (b) $4 + a = 9$ (c) $7x = 42$ (d) $5x + 4 = 19$

25 Umbrellas cost £4 each.
(a) Write a formula for the cost, C, in pounds, of u umbrellas.
(b) Find the value of u when $C = 28$.

26 (a) Find the value of $3m - 5$ when $m = 4$.
(b) $T = 3m - 5$. Find the value of m when $T = 4$.
(c) $P = 5y^2$. Find the value of P when $y = 3$.

27 John uses this rule:

Think of a number, subtract 3 and then double the result.

John's answer is 8.
What number did he start with?

28 (a) Find the value of $\dfrac{3(m + 9)}{n}$ when $m = -5$ and $n = 24$.

(b) Find the value of $3p + q$ when $p = -2$ and $q = 5$.

29 A sequence begins $1, -1, \ldots$
This rule is used to continue the sequence.

Multiply the last number by 2 and then subtract 3.

(a) What is the next term in the sequence?
(b) A term in the sequence is called x.
Write, in terms of x, the next term in the sequence.

30 Here is a formula for working out a printing cost.

printing cost	=	price per sheet of paper	×	number of sheets of paper	+	fixed charge

The price per sheet of paper is £0.04. 2500 sheets of paper are used. The fixed charge is £45.50.
Work out the printing cost. Edexcel

31 (a) Draw the line $y = 2x + 1$ for values of x from -1 to 2.
(b) The line $y = 2x + 1$ crosses the line $x = -5$ at P.
Give the coordinates of P.

32 Solve these equations.
(a) $2x + 6 = 14$ (b) $3g - 5 = 4$ (c) $10y = 5$ (d) $6 + 2y = 4$

33 Maureen thought of a number. She divided this number by 4. She then added 3.
Her answer was 9.
What number did Maureen think of? Edexcel

34 Jon cycled a distance of 18 km from Guildford to Cranleigh.
The graph shows Jon's cycle ride.
On the way, Jon stopped to buy a drink at a shop.

(a) (i) Write down the distance of the shop from Guildford.
(ii) Write down the time at which Jon stopped.
(iii) For how long did he stop?

Jon stayed at Cranleigh for lunch.
He left Cranleigh at 1.30 pm.
He cycled back to Guildford at a steady speed.
He reached Guildford at 3 pm.

(b) Work out the steady speed at which he cycled back to Guildford.

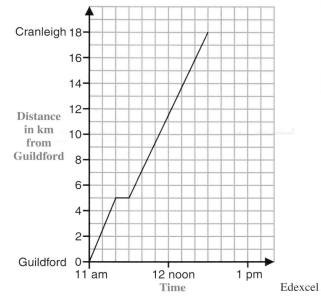

Edexcel

35 (a) Simplify (i) $5c + 2c - 3c$, (ii) $5p - 8r + 12r - 6p$.
(b) Find the value of
(i) $5x + 2y$ when $x = 3$ and $y = 6$,
(ii) $4g - 2h$ when $g = 2$ and $h = -4$.

Edexcel

36 (a) Solve the equations (i) $4(a - 2) = 6$, (ii) $5t + 3 = -1 + t$.
(b) The sum of the numbers x, $x - 3$ and $x + 7$ is 25.
By forming an equation in x, find the value of x.

37 (a) Solve $4p + 6 = 26$.
(b) Solve $5(2q + 6) = 25$.
(c) Solve $18y - 27 = 10y - 25$.

Edexcel

38 Here is a rule to change kilograms to pounds.

> Multiply the number of kilograms by 22 and then divide by 10.

(a) Use the rule to change 5 kilograms to pounds.
(b) Write a formula to change K kilograms to L pounds.
(c) Use your formula to find the value of K when $L = 55$.

39 (a) Factorise (i) $3a - 6$, (ii) $k^2 - 2k$.
(b) Multiply out (i) $5(x + 3)$, (ii) $m(m - 4)$.
(c) Solve (i) $3 - 4x = x + 8$, (ii) $3(2x + 1) = 6$.

40 (a) On the same diagram draw the graphs $2y = x + 4$ and $y = \frac{1}{2}x + 1$.
(b) What do you notice about the two lines you have drawn?

41 A shop sells Big lollipops at 80p each and Small lollipops at 60p each.
Henry buys x Big lollipops.
(a) Write down an expression, in terms of x, for the cost of Henry's lollipops.

Lucy buys r Big lollipops and t Small lollipops.
(b) Write down an expression, in terms of r and t, for the total cost of Lucy's lollipops.

The cost of g Big lollipops and 2 Small lollipops is £10.80.
(c) (i) Write this as an equation in terms of g.
(ii) Use your equation to find the value of g.

Edexcel

Angles

- You should be able to use a **protractor** to measure and draw angles accurately.

  Eg 1 Measure the size of this angle.

  vertex •

  The angle measures 30°.

  > To measure an angle, the protractor is placed so that its centre point is on the corner (vertex) of the angle, with the base along one of the arms of the angle, as shown.

- Types and names of angles.

Acute angle	Right angle	Obtuse angle	Reflex angle
			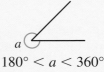
$0° < a < 90°$	$a = 90°$	$90° < a < 180°$	$180° < a < 360°$

- Angle properties.

Angles at a point	Complementary angles	Supplementary angles	Vertically opposite angles
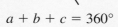		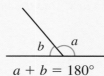	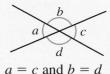
$a + b + c = 360°$	$x + y = 90°$	$a + b = 180°$	$a = c$ and $b = d$

- Lines which meet at right angles are **perpendicular** to each other.

- A straight line joining two points is called a **line segment**.

- Lines which never meet and are always the same distance apart are **parallel**.

- When two parallel lines are crossed by a **transversal** the following pairs of angles are formed.

  Corresponding angles

  $a = c$

  Alternate angles

  $b = c$

  Allied angles

  $b + d = 180°$

  > Arrowheads are used to show that lines are **parallel**.

- You should be able to use angle properties to solve problems involving lines and angles.

  Eg 2 Work out the size of the angles marked with letters. Give a reason for each answer.

  $a + 64° = 180°$ (supplementary angles)
  $a = 180° - 64° = 116°$

  $b = 64°$ (vertically opposite angles)
  $c = 64°$ (corresponding angles)

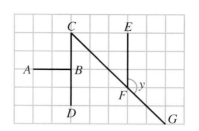

1 Look at the diagram.

   (a) Which lines are parallel to each other?
   (b) Which lines are perpendicular to each other?
   (c) (i) Measure angle *y*.
      (ii) Which of these words describes angle *y*?

      acute angle   obtuse angle   reflex angle

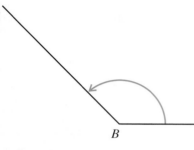

2   (a) Measure the size of angle *ABC*.

   (b) Copy the diagram.
      D is the point such that angle *BCD* is 102°
      and angle *BAD* is 68°.
      Mark the position of *D* on your diagram.

      Edexcel

3 Find the size of the lettered angles. Give a reason for each answer.

  (a) 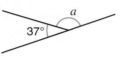   (b) 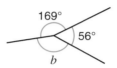   (c)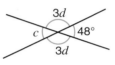

4   (a) (i) Work out the size of angle *p*.
      (ii) Give a reason for your answer.

   (b) (i) Work out the size of angle *q*.
      (ii) Give a reason for your answer.

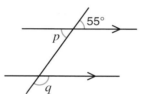

      Edexcel

5 In the diagram, the lines *PQ* and *RS* are parallel.

   (a) What is the size of angle *PQR*?
      Give a reason for your answer.

   (b) Find the size of angle *RQS*.

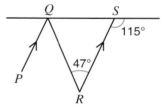

6 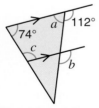 Work out the size of the angles marked with letters.
Give a reason for each answer.

7 Find the size of the angles marked with letters.

  (a)   (b) 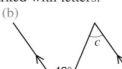   (c)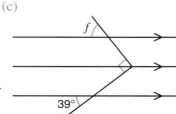

Triangles

What you need to know

- A **triangle** is a shape made by three straight sides.

- Triangles can be: **acute-angled** (all angles less than 90°),
  obtuse-angled (one angle greater than 90°),
  right-angled (one angle equal to 90°).

- The sum of the angles in a triangle is 180°.
  $a + b + c = 180°$

- The exterior angle is equal to the sum of the two opposite interior angles. $a + b = d$

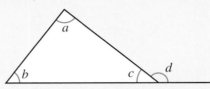

- Types of triangle:

Scalene **Isosceles** **Equilateral**

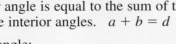

A **sketch** is used when an accurate drawing is not required. Dashes across lines show sides that are equal in length. Equal angles are marked using arcs.

- You should be able to use properties of triangles to solve problems.

  Eg 1 Find the size of the angles marked a and b.
  $a = 86° + 51°$ (ext. ∠ of a Δ)
  $a = 137°$
  $b + 137° = 180°$ (supp. ∠'s)
  $b = 43°$

- Perimeter of a triangle is the sum of its three sides.

- Area of a triangle $= \dfrac{\text{base} \times \text{perpendicular height}}{2}$

  $$A = \frac{1}{2} \times b \times h$$

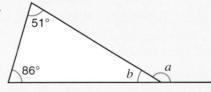

  Eg 2 Calculate the area of this triangle.
  $A = \dfrac{1}{2} \times b \times h$
  $= \dfrac{1}{2} \times 9 \times 6 \,\text{cm}^2$
  $= 27 \,\text{cm}^2$

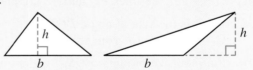

- You should be able to draw triangles accurately, using ruler, compasses and protractor.

Exercise 19

1 Without measuring, work out the size of the angles marked with letters.

(a) (b) (c)

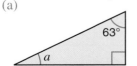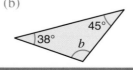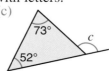

2 *ABC* and *EBD* are straight lines.
BD = *BC*. Angle *CBD* = 42°.

(a) Write down the size of the angle marked *e*°.

(b) Work out the size of the angle marked *f*°.

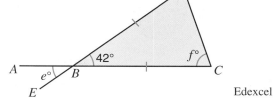

Edexcel

3

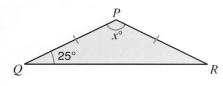

The diagram shows triangle *PQR*, with *PQ* = *PR*.
Work out the value of *x*.
Give a reason for your answer.

4 (a) (i) Write down the size of the angle marked *x*°.
(ii) Give a reason for your answer.

(b) (i) Work out the size of the angle marked *y*°.
(ii) Give a reason for your answer.

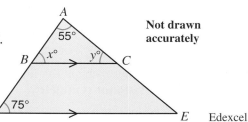

Not drawn accurately

Edexcel

5

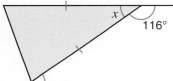

The diagram shows an isosceles triangle with two sides extended.

(a) Work out the size of angle *x*.

(b) Work out the size of angle *y*.

6 Make accurate drawings of these triangles using the information given.

(a)

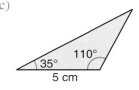

(b)

(c)

7 Find the areas of these triangles.

(a)

(b)

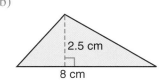

(c)

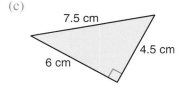

8

The diagram shows a sketch of a triangle.
(a) Make an accurate drawing of the triangle.
(b) (i) On your drawing, measure the size of the angle marked *x*°.
(ii) What is the special mathematical name of the angle marked *x*°?
(c) Work out the area of the triangle.

Edexcel

9 The diagram shows triangle *ABC*.
Calculate the area of triangle *ABC*.

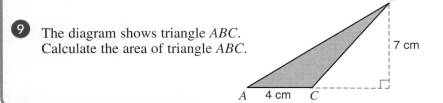

Triangles . . . . Triangles . . . Triangles . . . .

Symmetry and Congruence

- A two-dimensional shape has **line symmetry** if the line divides the shape so that one side fits exactly over the other.

- A two-dimensional shape has **rotational symmetry** if it fits into a copy of its outline as it is rotated through 360°.

- A shape is only described as having rotational symmetry if the order of rotational symmetry is 2 or more.

- The number of times a shape fits into its outline in a single turn is the **order of rotational symmetry**.

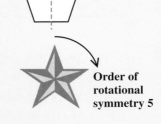

Order of rotational symmetry 5

Eg 1 For each of these shapes (a) draw and state the number of lines of symmetry,
(b) state the order of rotational symmetry.

(i)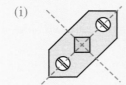

(ii)

(iii)

Two lines of symmetry.
Rotational symmetry of order 2.

4 lines of symmetry.
Order of rotational symmetry 4.

No lines of symmetry.
Order of rotational symmetry 1.
The shape is **not** described as
having rotational symmetry.

- A **plane of symmetry** slices through a three-dimensional object so that one half is the mirror image of the other half.

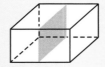

- Three-dimensional objects can have **axes of symmetry**.

Eg 2 Sketch a cuboid and show its axes of symmetry.

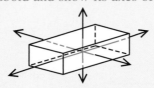

A cuboid has three axes of symmetry.
The order of rotational symmetry
about each axis is 2.

- When two shapes are the same shape and size they are said to be **congruent**.

- There are four ways to show that a pair of triangles are congruent.

SSS 3 corresponding sides.	**ASA**	2 angles and a corresponding side.
SAS 2 sides and the included angle.	**RHS**	Right angle, hypotenuse and one other side.

Eg 3 Which of these triangles are congruent to each other? Give a reason for your answer.

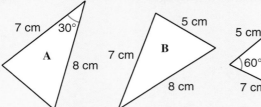

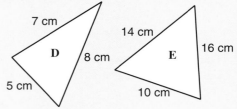

B and D.   Reason: 3 corresponding sides (SSS)

1 Copy and reflect each of the shapes in the mirror lines given.

(a)

(b)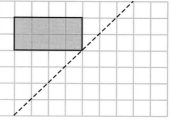

Edexcel

2 Consider the letters of the word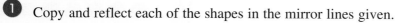

Which letters have (a) line symmetry only,
                       (b) rotational symmetry only,
                       (c) line symmetry and rotational symmetry?

3 For each of these shapes state (i) the number of lines of symmetry,
                                    (ii) the order of rotational symmetry.

(a)
(b)
(c)
(d)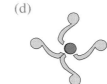

4

The diagram shows a square grid with two squares shaded.
Copy the diagram and shade two more squares so that the final diagram
has rotational symmetry of order 2.

5 The diagram represents a prism.

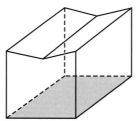

Copy the diagram and draw in one plane of symmetry on your diagram.

Edexcel

6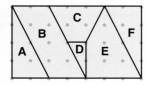

The diagram shows a rectangle which has been cut into 6 pieces.
Which two pieces are congruent to each other?

7 The diagram shows information about four triangles.
Which two triangles are congruent?
Give a reason for your answer.

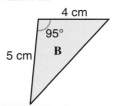

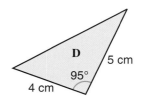

Quadrilaterals ● ● ● ● ● ● ● ● ●

What you need to know

● A **quadrilateral** is a shape made by four straight lines.

● The sum of the angles in a quadrilateral is 360°.

● The **perimeter** of a quadrilateral is the sum of the lengths of its four sides.

$$a + b + c + d = 360°$$

● Facts about these special quadrilaterals:

parallelogram   rectangle   square   rhombus   trapezium   isosceles trapezium   kite

Quadrilateral	Sides	Angles	Diagonals	Line symmetry	Order of rotational symmetry	Area formula
Parallelogram	Opposite sides equal and parallel	Opposite angles equal	Bisect each other	0	2	$A = bh$
Rectangle	Opposite sides equal and parallel	All 90°	Bisect each other	2	2	$A = bh$
Rhombus	4 equal sides, opposite sides parallel	Opposite angles equal	Bisect each other at 90°	2	2	$A = bh$
Square	4 equal sides, opposite sides parallel	All 90°	Bisect each other at 90°	4	4	$A = l^2$
Trapezium	1 pair of parallel sides					$A = \frac{1}{2}(a + b)h$
Isosceles trapezium	1 pair of parallel sides, non-parallel sides equal	2 pairs of equal angles	Equal in length	1	1*	$A = \frac{1}{2}(a + b)h$
Kite	2 pairs of adjacent sides equal	1 pair of opposite angles equal	One bisects the other at 90°	1	1*	

*A shape is only described as having rotational symmetry if the order of rotational symmetry is 2 or more.

● You should be able to use properties of quadrilaterals to solve problems.

Eg 1 Work out the size of the angle marked x.

Opposite angles are equal.
So, $125° + 125° + x + x = 360°$
$x = 55°$

Eg 2 Find the area of this trapezium.

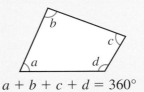

$A = \frac{1}{2}(a + b)h$

$= \frac{1}{2}(6 + 9)5$

$= \frac{1}{2} \times 15 \times 5$

$= 37.5 \text{ cm}^2$

● You should be able to construct a quadrilateral from given information using ruler, protractor, compasses.

44

1 This rectangle is drawn on 1 cm squared paper.
It has a perimeter of 18 cm.

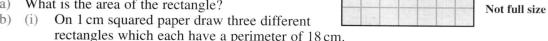

Not full size

  (a) What is the area of the rectangle?

  (b) (i)   On 1 cm squared paper draw three different
           rectangles which each have a perimeter of 18 cm.

      (ii) Find the area of each rectangle.

2 (a) Name each quadrilateral which has all its sides of equal length.

    (b) Name each quadrilateral which has only one pair of parallel sides.

    (c) Name each quadrilateral which has two pairs of parallel sides,
        but no angles of 90° between its sides.

Edexcel

3 Find the size of the lettered angles.

  (a)   (b)   (c)

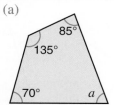 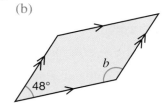 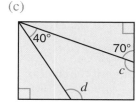

4 (a) (i)   Work out the value of x.

        (ii) Give a reason for your answer.

    (b) (i)   Work out the value of y.

        (ii) Give a reason for your answer.

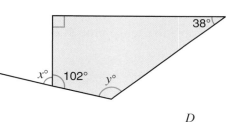

Edexcel

5 The diagram shows a quadrilateral $ABCD$.
$AB = BC$ and $CD = DA$.

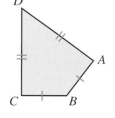

  (a) Which of the following correctly describes the quadrilateral $ABCD$?
     rhombus   **parallelogram**   **kite**   **trapezium**

  (b) Angle $ADC = 36°$ and angle $BCD = 105°$.
     Work out the size of angle ABC.

6 $ABCD$ is a quadrilateral.
$AB = 6$ cm, $AC = 9$ cm, $BC = 5$ cm, $AD = 3.5$ cm and angle $BAD = 66°$.
Make an accurate drawing of the quadrilateral $ABCD$.

Edexcel

7 A rectangle measures 8.6 cm by 6.4 cm.

  (a) Find the perimeter of the rectangle.

  (b) Find the area of the rectangle.

8 The perimeter of this rectangle is 22 cm.
The length of the rectangle is 8 cm.
Work out the area of the rectangle.

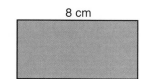

8 cm

Edexcel

9

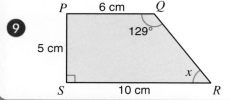

The diagram shows a trapezium $PQRS$.

  (a) Work out the size of the angle marked x.

  (b) Calculate the area of the trapezium.

Polygons

What you need to know

- A **polygon** is a many-sided shape made by straight lines.

- A polygon with all sides equal and all angles equal is called a **regular polygon**.

- Shapes you need to know: A 3-sided polygon is called a **triangle**.
  A 4-sided polygon is called a **quadrilateral**.
  A 5-sided polygon is called a **pentagon**.
  A 6-sided polygon is called a **hexagon**.

- The sum of the exterior angles of any polygon is 360°.

- At each vertex of a polygon: interior angle + exterior angle = 180°

- The sum of the interior angles of an n-sided polygon is given by:
  $(n - 2) \times 180°$

- For a regular n-sided polygon: exterior angle $= \dfrac{360°}{n}$

- You should be able to use the properties of polygons to solve problems.

interior angle
exterior angle

| **Eg 1** | Find the sum of the interior angles of a pentagon.
$(5 - 2) \times 180° = 3 \times 180° = 540°$ | A pentagon has 5 sides, so substitute $n = 5$ into $(n - 2) \times 180°$. |

Eg 2   A regular polygon has an exterior angle of 30°.
   (a)   How many sides has the polygon?
   (b)   What is the size of an interior angle of the polygon?

(a) $n = \dfrac{360°}{\text{exterior angle}}$
   $n = \dfrac{360°}{30°}$
   $n = 12$

(b)   int. $\angle$ + ext. $\angle$ = 180°
   int. $\angle$ + 30° = 180°
   interior angle = 150°

- A shape will **tessellate** if it covers a surface without overlapping and leaves no gaps.

- All triangles tessellate.

- All quadrilaterals tessellate.

- Equilateral triangles, squares and hexagons can be used to make **regular tessellations**.

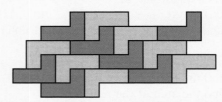

Exercise 22

1   Work out the size of the angles marked with letters.

(a)
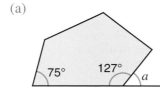
75°   127° a

(b)
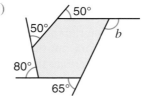
50°
50° b
80°
65°

(c)
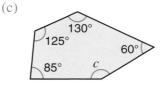
130°
125°   60°
85° c

2 These shapes are drawn on isometric paper.

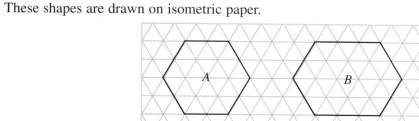

(a) What are the differences between the symmetry of shape *A* and the symmetry of shape *B*?
(b) Copy shape *A* onto isometric paper and then draw five more shapes to show how the shape tessellates.

3 These shapes are regular polygons. Work out the size of the lettered angles.

(a)  (b) 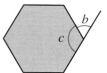 (c)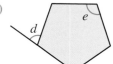

4 *ABCDEF* is a regular hexagon with centre *O*.
(a) What type of triangle is *ABO*?
(b) (i) Work out the size of the angle marked $x°$.
 (ii) Work out the size of the angle marked $y°$.
(c) (i) What type of quadrilateral is *BCDO*?
 (ii) Draw a diagram to show how three such quadrilaterals can tessellate to make a hexagon.

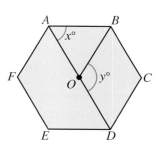

Edexcel

5 The diagram shows part of a regular polygon.
The exterior angles of this polygon are 24°.
How many sides has the polygon?

6 Four regular pentagons are placed together, as shown, to form a rhombus, *ABCD*.

Calculate the size of
(a) angle *ABC*,
(b) angle *XCY*.

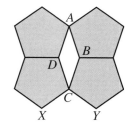

7

The diagram shows a hexagon.
Show that the sum of the interior angles of a hexagon is 720°.

8 The diagram shows part of an inscribed regular polygon.
The line *AB* is one side of the polygon.
O is the centre of the circle.
Angle $AOB = 30°$.

Show that the polygon has 12 sides and hence find the sum of its interior angles.

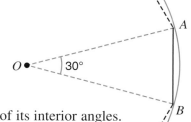

What you need to know

- **Compass points**

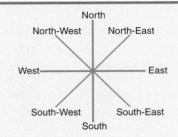

  > The angle between North and East is 90°.
  > The angle between North and North-East is 45°.

- **Bearings** are used to describe the direction in which you must travel to get from one place to another.

- A bearing is an angle measured from the North line in a clockwise direction.
  A bearing can be any angle from 0° to 360° and is written as a three-figure number.

  > To find a bearing:
  >   measure angle *a* to find the bearing of *Y* from *X*,
  >   measure angle *b* to find the bearing of *X* from *Y*.

  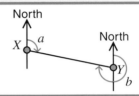

- You should be able to use **scales** and **bearings** to interpret and draw accurate diagrams.

  > There are two ways to describe a scale.
  > 1. A scale of 1 cm to 10 km means that a distance of 1 cm on the map represents an actual distance of 10 km.
  > 2. A scale of 1 : 10 000 means that all distances measured on the map have to be multiplied by 10 000 to find the real distance.

Eg 1 The diagram shows the plan of a stage in a car rally.
The plan has been drawn to a scale of 1 : 50 000.

(a) What is the bearing of *Q* from *P*?
(b) What is the bearing of *P* from *R*?
(c) What is the actual distance from
    P to *R* in metres?

(a) 080°
(b) 295°
(c) 3500 m

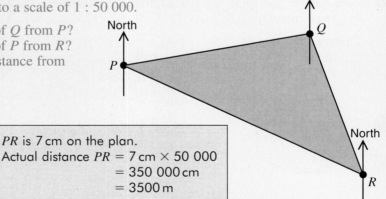

PR is 7 cm on the plan.
Actual distance *PR* = 7 cm × 50 000
                     = 350 000 cm
                     = 3500 m

Exercise 23

 Jon is facing North-West.
He turns through 180°.
In which direction is he now facing?

2 Here is a plan of a town.
Some buildings are shown on it.

Write down the compass bearing of
(a) the Office block from the Castle,
(b) the Windmill from the Office block,
(c) the Church form the Castle.

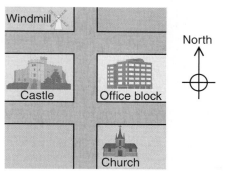

Edexcel

3 A bridge is 2600 m in length.
A plan of the bridge has been drawn to a scale of 1 cm to 100 m.
What is the length of the bridge on the plan?

4 The dot represents a lighthouse.
The cross represents a ship.

Measure the 3-figure bearing
of the ship from the lighthouse.

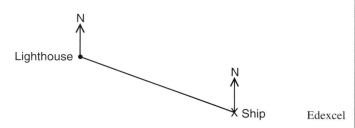

Edexcel

5

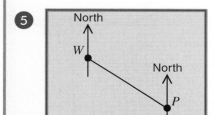

The map shows the positions of a windmill, *W*, and a pylon, *P*.
(a) What is the bearing of
　(i) the pylon from the windmill,
　(ii) the windmill from the pylon?

The map has been drawn to a scale of 2 cm to 5 km.
(b) Use the map to find the distance *WP* in kilometres.

6 The map shows part of a coastline and a coastguard station.
1 cm on the map represents 2 km.
A ship is 12 km from the coastguard station on a bearing of 160°.
Copy the map and plot the position of the ship from the coastguard station, using a scale of
1 cm to represent 2 km.

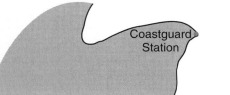

Edexcel

7 The diagram shows a sketch of the course to be used for a running event.

(a) Draw an accurate plan of the course, using a
scale of 1 cm to represent 100 m.

(b) Use your plan to find
　(i) the bearing of *X* from *Y*,
　(ii) the distance *XY* in metres.

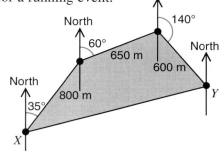

What you need to know

- A **circle** is the shape drawn by keeping a pencil the same distance from a fixed point on a piece of paper.

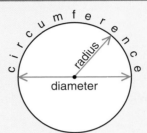

- The meaning of the following words:
  Circumference – special name used for the perimeter of a circle.

  Radius – distance from the centre of a circle to any point on the circumference.
  The plural of radius is **radii**.

  Diameter – distance right across the circle, passing through the centre point. The diameter is twice as long as the radius.

  Chord – a line joining two points on the circumference.
  The longest chord is the diameter.

  Tangent – a line which touches the circumference of a circle at one point only.

  Arc – part of the circumference of a circle.

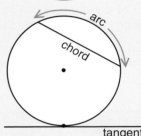

- The **circumference** of a circle is given by: $\boxed{C = \pi \times d \quad \text{or} \quad C = 2 \times \pi \times r}$

- The **area** of a circle is given by: $\boxed{A = \pi \times r^2}$

- You should be able to solve problems which involve finding the circumference or the area of a circle.

  Eg 1 A circle has a radius of 4 cm.
  Estimate: (a) the circumference of the circle, (b) the area of the circle.

  (a) $C = 2 \times \pi \times r$ (b) $A = \pi \times r \times r$
  $C = 2 \times 3 \times 4$ $A = 3 \times 4 \times 4$ | When **estimating**, take π to be 3. |
  $C = 24$ cm $A = 48$ cm^2

  | For more accurate calculations, take π to be 3.14 or use the π key on your calculator. |

  Eg 2 Calculate the circumference of   **Eg 3** Calculate the area of a circle with
  a circle with diameter 18 cm.   diameter 12 cm.
  Give your answer to 1 d.p.   Give your answer to the nearest whole number.

  $C = \pi \times d$ $A = \pi \times r^2$
  $C = \pi \times 18$ $A = \pi \times 6 \times 6$ | $r = \dfrac{\text{diameter}}{2}$ |
  $C = 56.548...$ $A = 113.097...$
  $C = 56.5$ cm, correct to 1 d.p. $A = 113$ cm^2, to the nearest whole number.

Exercise 24

Do not use a calculator for question 1.

1 A circular pond has a diameter of 9.8 metres.
  (a) Estimate the circumference of the pond.
  (b) Estimate the area of the pond.

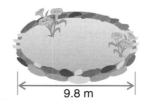

9.8 m

Questions 2 to 10. Take π to be 3.14 or use the π key on your calculator.

2 A circle has a diameter of 5 cm.
   (a) Calculate the circumference of the circle.
   (b) Calculate the area of the circle.
   Give your answers correct to one decimal place.

3 A table has a top in the shape of a circle with a radius of
   45 centimetres.
   Calculate the area of the circular table top.

Edexcel

4 A circle has a radius of 32 cm.
   Work out the circumference of the circle.
   Give your answer correct to the nearest centimetre.

Edexcel

5 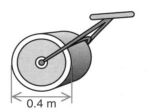 Tranter has completed three-fifths of a circular jigsaw puzzle.
   The puzzle has a radius of 20 cm.
   What area of the puzzle is complete?

6 Mr Kray's lawn is 25 m in length.
   He rolls it with a garden roller.
   The garden roller has a diameter of 0.4 m.
   Work out the number of times the roller rotates when
   rolling the length of the lawn once.

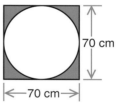

7 The radius of a circle is 5.1 m.
   Work out the area of the circle.

Edexcel

8 The diagram shows a circle of diameter 70 cm
   inside a square of side 70 cm.
   Work out the area of the shaded part of the diagram.

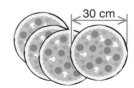

Edexcel

9 Each wheel on Hannah's bicycle has a radius of 15 cm.
   Calculate how many complete revolutions each wheel makes when Hannah cycles 100 metres.

10 Discs of card are used in the packaging of frozen pizzas.
   Each disc fits the base of the pizza exactly.

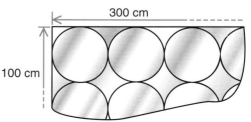

   (a) Calculate the area of a disc used to pack a large pizza
       with a diameter of 30 cm.

   (b) The discs for large pizzas are cut from
       sheets of card 300 cm by 100 cm.
       (i) How many discs can be cut from
           each sheet?
       (ii) What area of each sheet is wasted?

Circles . . . . Circles . . . . Circles . . . .

24

51

Area and Volume ●●●●●●●●

What you need to know

- **Faces**, **vertices** (corners) and **edges**.

  A cube has 6 faces, 8 vertices and 12 edges.

  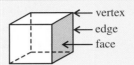

- A **net** can be used to make a solid shape.

  Eg 1 Draw a net of a cube.

- **Isometric paper** is used to make 2-dimensional drawings of 3-dimensional shapes.

  Eg 2 Draw a cube of edge 2 cm on isometric paper.

- **Plans and Elevations**

  The view of a 3-dimensional shape looking from above is called a **plan**.
  The view of a 3-dimensional shape from the front or sides is called an **elevation**.

  Eg 3 Draw diagrams to show the plan and elevation from **X**, for this 3-dimensional shape.

  plan   **elevation X**

  Dotted lines are used to show hidden edges.

- **Volume** is the amount of space occupied by a 3-dimensional shape.

- The formula for the volume of a **cuboid** is:
  Volume = length × breadth × height
  $$V = l \times b \times h$$

  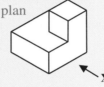

- Volume of a **cube** is: $V = l^3$

- To find the **surface area** of a cuboid, find the areas of the 6 rectangular faces and add the answers together.

  Eg 4 Find the volume and surface area of a cuboid measuring 7 cm by 5 cm by 3 cm.

  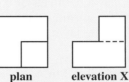

  Volume = $l \times b \times h$
  = 7 cm × 5 cm × 3 cm
  = 105 cm³

  Surface area = (2 × 7 × 5) + (2 × 5 × 3) + (2 × 3 × 7)
  = 70 + 30 + 42
  = 142 cm²

- Shapes formed by joining different shapes together are called **compound shapes**.
  To find the area of a compound shape we must first split the shape up into rectangles, squares and triangles. Find the area of each part and then add the answers together.

  Eg 5 Find the total area of this shape.

  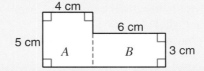

  Area A = 5 × 4 = 20 cm²
  Area B = 6 × 3 = 18 cm²
  Total area = 20 + 18 = 38 cm²

1 This shape is a pyramid.

(a) How many faces, edges and vertices has the pyramid?

(b) Which of these nets is a net of the pyramid?

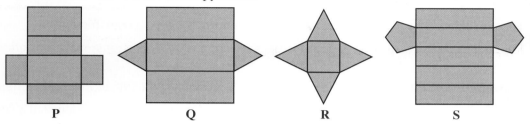

P   Q   R   S

2 The diagram shows a solid drawn on isometric paper.

(a) Draw the plan of the solid.

(b) Draw the elevation of the solid from the direction shown by the arrow.

3

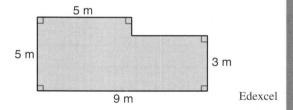

Not full size

This shape has been drawn on 1 cm squared paper.

(a) Find the perimeter of the shape.

(b) Find the area of the shape.

(c) On 1 cm squared paper, draw a rectangle with the same perimeter.

4 This diagram shows the floor plan of a room. Work out the area of the floor.

5 m

5 m   3 m

9 m   Edexcel

5

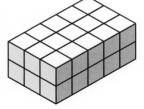

This cuboid has been made using cubes of side 1 cm.

(a) How many cubes are needed to make the cuboid?

(b) (i) Draw a net of the cuboid on 1 cm squared paper.
     (ii) Hence, find the surface area of the cuboid.

6 The diagram represents the babies' pool, with paving around, at a leisure centre. The pool is rectangular, 8 m long by 5 m wide and has a depth of 0.6 m throughout.

(a) Work out the volume of the pool in m³.

The paving around the pool is 2 m wide.

(b) Work out the area of the paving.

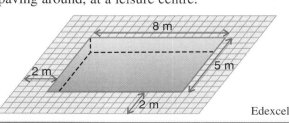

8 m

2 m   5 m

2 m   Edexcel

Transformations

What you need to know

- The movement of a shape from one position to another is called a **transformation**.

- **Single transformations** can be described in terms of a reflection, a rotation, a translation or an enlargement.

- **Reflection**: The image of the shape is the same distance from the mirror line as the original.

- **Rotation**: All points are turned through the same angle about the same point, called a centre of rotation.

- **Translation**: All points are moved the same distance in the same direction without turning.

- **Enlargement**: All lengths are multiplied by a scale factor.

$$\text{Scale factor} = \frac{\text{new length}}{\text{original length}}$$

$$\boxed{\text{New length} = \text{scale factor} \times \text{original length}}$$

- You should be able to draw the transformation of a shape.

Eg 1 Draw the image of triangle P after it has been translated 3 units to the left and 2 units up.

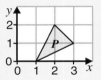 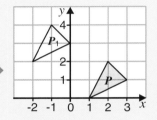

- You should be able to fully describe transformations.

Transformation	Image same shape and size?	Details needed to describe the transformation
Reflection	Yes	Mirror line, sometimes given as an equation.
Rotation	Yes	Centre of rotation, amount of turn, direction of turn.
Translation	Yes	Horizontal movement and vertical movement.
Enlargement	No	Centre of enlargement, scale factor.

Eg 2 Describe the single transformation which maps

    (a) A onto B,   (b) A onto C,   (c) A onto D,   (d) A onto E.

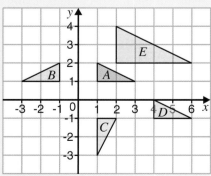

    (a) **reflection** in the y axis.
    (b) **rotation** of 90° clockwise about the origin.
    (c) **translation** 3 units to the right and 2 units down.
    (d) **enlargement** scale factor 2, centre (0, 0).

1 Copy each diagram and draw the transformation given.

   (a) Reflect the shape in the *x* axis.

   (b) Translate the shape, 2 units left and 3 units up.

   (c) Rotate the shape, 180° about the origin.

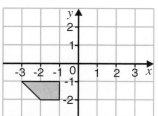 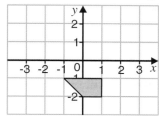 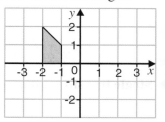

2 In each diagram *A* is mapped onto *B* by a single transformation. Describe each transformation.

   (a)   (b)   (c)

3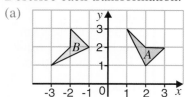

   On squared paper, enlarge *ABCD* by a scale factor of 2.

Edexcel

4 (a) On squared paper, draw triangle *ABC* with vertices at: *A* (1, 1), *B* (2, 3) and *C* (4, 2).

   (b) Triangle *ABC* is reflected in the *y* axis. Draw the triangle in its new position.

5 Copy the diagram.
Rotate the triangle through 90° **clockwise** about the point (0, 0).
Draw the triangle in its new position.

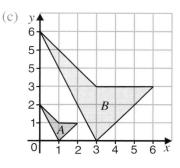

Edexcel

6 The diagram shows the positions of kites *P*, *Q* and *R*.

   (a) *P* is mapped onto *Q* by a reflection.
      What is the equation of the line of reflection?

   (b) *P* is mapped onto *R* by a translation.
      Describe the translation.

   (c) *P* is mapped onto *S* by an enlargement, scale factor 3, centre (0, 0).
      Copy *P* onto a grid and draw the position of *S*.

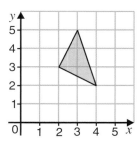
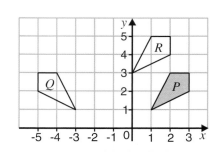

Understanding and Using Measures

What you need to know

- The common units — both **metric** and **imperial** — used to measure **length**, **mass** and **capacity**.

- How to estimate measurements using sensible units and a suitable degree of accuracy.

- How to convert from one unit to another. This includes knowing the connection between one metric unit and another and the approximate equivalents between metric and imperial units.

Metric Units	Imperial Units	Conversions
Length 1 kilometre (km) = 1000 metres (m) 1 m = 100 centimetres (cm) 1 cm = 10 mm	**Length** 1 foot = 12 inches 1 yard = 3 feet	**Length** 5 miles is about 8 km 1 inch is about 2.5 cm 1 foot is about 30 cm
Mass 1 tonne (t) = 1000 kilograms (kg) 1 kg = 1000 grams (g)	**Mass** 1 pound = 16 ounces 14 pounds = 1 stone	**Mass** 1 kg is about 2.2 pounds
Capacity and volume 1 litre = 1000 millilitres (ml) 1 cm³ = 1 ml	**Capacity and volume** 1 gallon = 8 pints	**Capacity and volume** 1 litre is about 1.75 pints 1 gallon is about 4.5 litres

- How to change between units of area.   For example $1 \, m^2 = 10\,000 \, cm^2$.

- How to change between units of volume.   For example $1 \, m^3 = 1\,000\,000 \, cm^3$.

- You should be able to solve problems involving different units.

  Eg 1 A tank holds 6 gallons of water.
  How many litres is this? $6 \times 4.5 = 27$ litres

  Eg 2 A cuboid measures 1.5 m by 90 cm by 80 cm.
  Calculate the volume of the cuboid, in m^3. $1.5 \times 0.9 \times 0.8 = 1.08 \, m^3$

- Be able to read scales accurately.

- **Speed** is a measurement of how fast something is travelling.
  It involves two other measures, **distance** and **time**.
  In situations where speed is not constant, **average speed** is used.

  $$\text{Speed} = \frac{\text{Distance}}{\text{Time}}$$ $$\text{Average speed} = \frac{\text{Total distance travelled}}{\text{Total time taken}}$$

  The formula linking speed, distance and time can be rearranged and remembered as:
  $$S = D \div T$$
  $$D = S \times T$$
  $$T = D \div S$$

- You should be able to solve problems involving speed, distance and time.

  Eg 3 Wyn takes 2 hours to run 24 km.
  Calculate his speed in kilometres per hour.

  $$\text{Speed} = \frac{\text{Distance}}{\text{Time}} = \frac{24}{2} = 12 \, km/h$$

  Eg 4 Norrie says, "If I drive at an average speed of 60 km/h it will take me $2\frac{1}{2}$ hours to complete my journey." What distance is his journey?

  $$\text{Distance} = \text{Speed} \times \text{Time} = 60 \times 2\frac{1}{2} = 150 \, km$$

1 What value is shown by the pointer on each of these diagrams?

(a)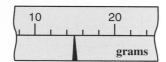

(b)

(c)

2 Write down the name of a unit which is used to measure
(a) the length of a garden,
(b) the amount of petrol in a car's petrol tank,
(c) the area of a school playing field,
(d) the weight of a calculator.

Edexcel

3

The diagram shows a man standing next to a tram. The man is of average height.
Estimate the length of the tram. Give your answer in metres.

Edexcel

4 Write each of the following using a more suitable unit.
(a) The distance between two towns is 6000 metres.
(b) A mouse weighs 0.06 kilograms.
(c) A piece of paper has an area of $0.006 \, \text{m}^2$.
(d) A room has a volume of $60\,000\,000 \, \text{cm}^3$.

5 A rectangular doormat measures 150 cm by 120 cm.
Calculate the area of the doormat in square metres.

6 (a) How many kilometres are the same as 40 miles?
(b) How many miles are the same as 40 kilometres?

7 The tank in Laura's car holds 12 gallons of petrol.
How many litres is 12 gallons?

8 Mum's Traditional Jam is sold in two sizes.
A 1 lb pot of jam costs 71 pence. A 1 kg pot of jam costs £1.50.
Which pot of jam is better value for money? You must show all your working.

9 Debbie is 5 feet 4 inches tall and weighs 9 stone 2 lb. Joyce is 155 cm tall and weighs 60 kg.
Who is taller? Who is heavier? You must show your working.

10 Norma travels 128 km in 2 hours. Calculate her average speed in kilometres per hour.

11 Sean cycled 24 km at an average speed of 16 km/h. How long did he take?

12 Ahmed takes $2\frac{1}{2}$ hours to drive to London. He averages 66 km/h. What distance does he drive?

13 A lorry takes $1\frac{1}{2}$ hours to travel 60 miles.
Calculate the average speed of the lorry in miles per hour.

Section Review – Shape, Space and Measures

1 The diagram shows a four-sided shape, *ABCD*.

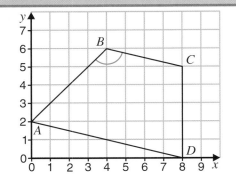

(a) What are the coordinates of
 (i) point *B*,
 (ii) the midpoint of *AD*?
(b) Which two lines are parallel?
(c) (i) Measure and write down the size of angle *B*.
 (ii) What is the mathematical name for angle *B*?

2

A B C

The diagram shows some 3-dimensional shapes.

(a) How many edges has shape *A*?
(b) How many faces has shape *B*?
(c) What is the mathematical name for shape *C*?

3 Each small square on the grid has a side of 1 cm.

(a) Work out the area of the shaded shape.
(b) Work out the perimeter of the shaded shape.

Not full size

Edexcel

4

In which compass direction is

(a) the Post Office from the Cinema,
(b) the Cinema from the Church?

Edexcel

5 (a) Which of these weights are the same?
 8000 g   80 kg   800 g   8 kg   0.08 kg
(b) Which of these lengths is the longest?
 0.2 km   20 m   2000 mm   200 cm
(c) The scales show weights in kilograms.
 Write down the weight of the pears.

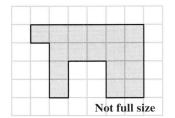

6

This solid has been made using 1 cm cubes.

(a) What is the volume of the solid?
(b) (i) Draw the plan of the solid.
 (ii) Draw the elevation of the solid from the direction shown by the arrow.

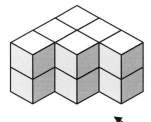

7 Copy the diagram.
Draw the reflection of the shape in the mirror line.

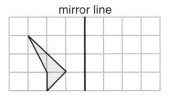

mirror line

8 (a) Here is a pattern of regular octagons and squares. Explain why these shapes tessellate.
(b) Draw a tessellation which uses equilateral triangles and regular hexagons.

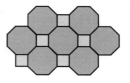

9 Find the angles marked with letters. Give a reason for each of your answers.

(a)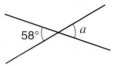

(b)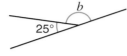

(c)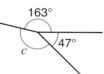

10 The diagram shows points A, B and C.

(a) What are the coordinates of A?
(b) What are the coordinates of C?
(c) $ABCD$ is a square.
What are the coordinates of D?

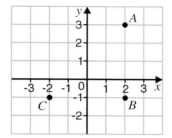

11 Here are 4 shapes labelled **A** to **D**.

A   B   C   D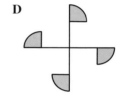

(a) (i) Copy the diagrams and draw in any lines of symmetry on the shapes.
(ii) Explain how you could check whether or not a line of symmetry was correct.
(b) Write **TRUE** or **FALSE** for each of the following statements.
(i) Shape **A** has rotational symmetry of order 2 or more.
(ii) Shape **B** has rotational symmetry of order 2 or more.
(iii) Shape **C** has rotational symmetry of order 2 or more.
(iv) Shape **D** has rotational symmetry of order 2 or more.

Edexcel

12 Two hospitals are 20 miles apart.
What is the distance between the hospitals in kilometres?

13 The diagram shows a pyramid with a square base.
The base of the pyramid is a square with edges of length 6 cm.
The length of each sloping edge of the pyramid is 5 cm.

(a) Make a sketch of a suitable net for the pyramid.
(b) Make an accurate full-size drawing of one of the triangular faces of the pyramid.

Edexcel

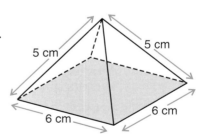

14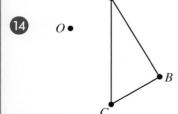

Triangle ABC is mapped onto triangle PQR, by an enlargement, centre O, scale factor 3.
Copy the diagram and draw triangle PQR.

15 Find the size of the angles *a*, *b* and *c*. Give a reason for each of your answers.

(a)

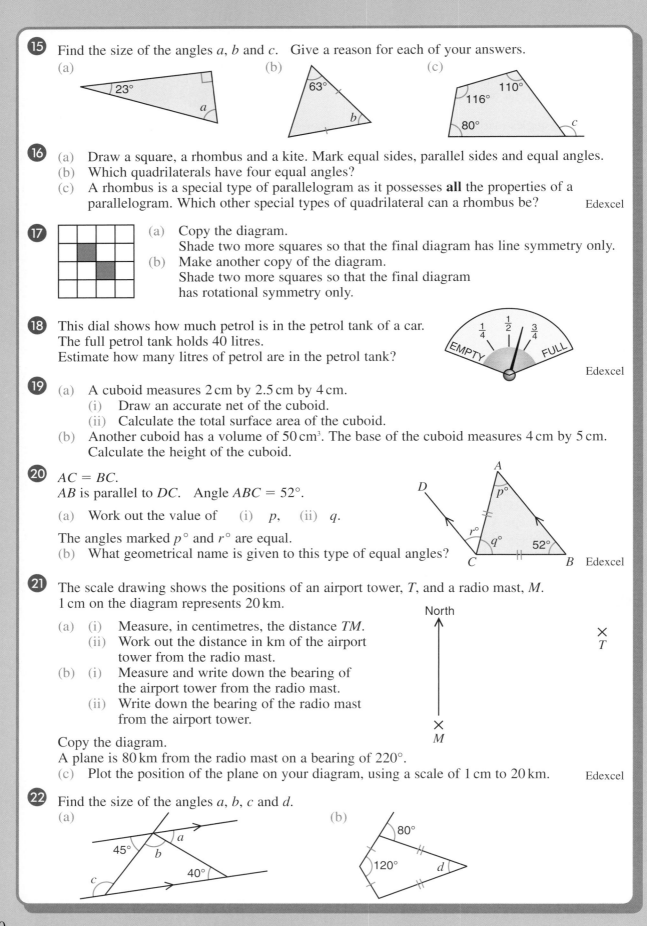

23°

a

(b)

63°

b

(c)

110°

116°

80°

c

16 (a) Draw a square, a rhombus and a kite. Mark equal sides, parallel sides and equal angles.
(b) Which quadrilaterals have four equal angles?
(c) A rhombus is a special type of parallelogram as it possesses **all** the properties of a parallelogram. Which other special types of quadrilateral can a rhombus be?   Edexcel

17
(a) Copy the diagram.
Shade two more squares so that the final diagram has line symmetry only.
(b) Make another copy of the diagram.
Shade two more squares so that the final diagram has rotational symmetry only.

18 This dial shows how much petrol is in the petrol tank of a car.
The full petrol tank holds 40 litres.
Estimate how many litres of petrol are in the petrol tank?

$\frac{1}{4}$ $\frac{1}{2}$ $\frac{3}{4}$

EMPTY   FULL

Edexcel

19 (a) A cuboid measures 2 cm by 2.5 cm by 4 cm.
(i) Draw an accurate net of the cuboid.
(ii) Calculate the total surface area of the cuboid.
(b) Another cuboid has a volume of 50 cm³. The base of the cuboid measures 4 cm by 5 cm. Calculate the height of the cuboid.

20 *AC* = *BC*.
AB is parallel to *DC*. Angle *ABC* = 52°.

(a) Work out the value of   (i) *p*,   (ii) *q*.

The angles marked *p*° and *r*° are equal.
(b) What geometrical name is given to this type of equal angles?

A
p°
D
r°
q°
C
52°
B   Edexcel

21 The scale drawing shows the positions of an airport tower, *T*, and a radio mast, *M*.
1 cm on the diagram represents 20 km.

(a) (i) Measure, in centimetres, the distance *TM*.
(ii) Work out the distance in km of the airport tower from the radio mast.
(b) (i) Measure and write down the bearing of the airport tower from the radio mast.
(ii) Write down the bearing of the radio mast from the airport tower.

North

×
T

×
M

Copy the diagram.
A plane is 80 km from the radio mast on a bearing of 220°.
(c) Plot the position of the plane on your diagram, using a scale of 1 cm to 20 km.   Edexcel

22 Find the size of the angles *a*, *b*, *c* and *d*.

(a)

45°
a
b
40°
c

(b)

80°
120°
d

23 The diagram shows the positions of shapes *P*, *Q* and *R*.

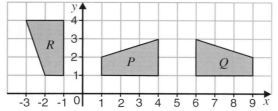

(a) Describe the single transformation which takes *P* onto *Q*.
(b) Describe the single transformation which takes *P* onto *R*.

Copy shape *P* onto squared paper.
(c) *P* is translated 3 units to the left and 2 units up.
    (i) Draw the new position of *P* on your diagram. Label it *S*.
    (ii) Describe the translation which takes *S* back onto *P*.

24 Colin is 5 feet 10 inches tall and weighs 11 stones.
On a medical form he is asked to give his height in centimetres and his weight in kilograms.
What values should he give?

25 Work out the area of each shape.

(a)

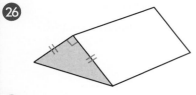

3 cm
12 cm

(b)

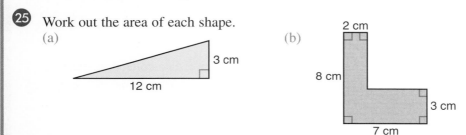

2 cm
8 cm
3 cm
7 cm

26

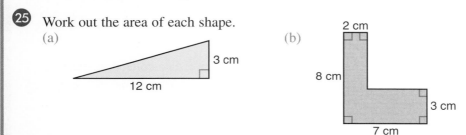

The diagram represents a prism.
The cross section (shaded region) of the prism is a
right-angled isosceles triangle.
Copy the diagram and draw one plane of symmetry of the prism.

Edexcel

27 The radius of a circle is 8 cm. Work out the area of the circle.

Edexcel

28 Gail leaves home at 0930 to cycle to the park.
She cycles at an average speed of 12 km/h and reaches the park at 0945.
How far is the park from her home?

29 The diagram shows the angle formed when three regular polygons are placed together, as shown.

(a) Explain why angle *a* is 120°.
(b) Work out the size of the angle marked *b*.

30

The top of a table is a circle with a radius of 55 cm.
(a) Calculate the circumference of the table top.

On the table are 6 place mats.
Each place mat is a circle with a diameter of 18 cm.
(b) What area of the table top is **not** covered by place mats?

Collection and Organisation of Data

What you need to know

- **Primary data** is data collected by an individual or organisation to use for a particular purpose. Primary data is obtained from experiments, investigations, surveys and by using questionnaires.

- **Secondary data** is data which is already available or has been collected by someone else for a different purpose. Sources of secondary data include the Annual Abstract of Statistics, Social Trends and the Internet.

- **Qualitative** data – Data which can only be described in words.

- **Quantitative** data – Data that has a numerical value. Quantitative data is either **discrete** or **continuous**. **Discrete** data can only take certain values. **Continuous** data has no exact value and is measurable.

- **Data Collection Sheets** – Used to record data during a survey.

- **Tally** – A way of recording each item of data on a data collection sheet.

    A group of five is recorded as ⊦⊦⊦⊦.

- **Frequency Table** – A way of collating the information recorded on a data collection sheet.

- **Grouped Frequency Table** – Used for continuous data or for discrete data when a lot of data has to be recorded.

- **Database** – A collection of data.

- **Class Interval** – The width of the groups used in a grouped frequency distribution.

- **Questionnaire** – A set of questions used to collect data for a survey. Questionnaires should:
    (1) use simple language,
    (2) ask short questions which can be answered precisely,
    (3) provide tick boxes,
    (4) avoid open-ended questions,
    (5) avoid leading questions,
    (6) ask questions in a logical order.

- **Hypothesis** – A hypothesis is a statement which may or may not be true.

- When information is required about a large group of people it is not always possible to survey everyone and only a **sample** may be asked.
  The sample chosen should be large enough to make the results meaningful and representative of the whole group (population).

- **Two-way Tables** – A way of illustrating two features of a survey.

Exercise 28

1 The table shows information about pupils in the same class at a school.

Name	Gender	Month of birth	Day of birth
Corrin	F	June	Monday
Daniel	M	March	Thursday
Laila	F	May	Friday
Ria	F	March	Tuesday
Miles	M	April	Tuesday

(a) Who was born in May?
(b) Who was born on a Tuesday in March?
(c) Which of these pupils is most likely to be the youngest? Give a reason for your answer.

2 Tayfan is organising a skiing holiday to Italy for his friends.

They can go to Cervinia, Livigno or Tonale. He asks each of his friends which resort they would like to go to and records the answers in his notebook.

Cervinia	Cervinia	Livigno	Tonale
Tonale	Tonale	Livigno	Cervinia
Livigno	Cervinia	Tonale	Tonale
Cervinia	Livigno	Tonale	Livigno
Tonale	Cervinia	Livigno	Tonale
Livigno	Tonale	Cervinia	

Show a better way of recording this information.

3 Meeta is doing a survey about sport.
She asks the question, "Do you play football, rugby or hockey?"
(a) Give a reason why this is not a suitable question.
(b) Write a similar question which is suitable.

4 Here are the weights, in kg, of 30 students.

45 52 56 65 34 45 67 65 34 45 65 87 45 34 56
54 45 67 84 45 67 45 56 76 57 84 35 64 58 60

(a) Copy and complete the frequency table below using a class interval of 10, starting at 30.

Weight range (w)	Tally	Frequency
$30 \leqslant w < 40$		

(b) Which class interval has the highest frequency?

Edexcel

5 A newspaper headline states:

> More students eat less for breakfast.

You are asked to investigate this headline.
Design an observation sheet to collect the data you need.
Invent the first 10 entries on your data sheet.

6 50 pupils are going on an educational visit. The pupils have to choose to go to one of:

the theatre   or   **the art gallery**   or   **the science museum**.

23 of the pupils are boys.
11 of the girls choose to visit the theatre.
9 of the girls choose to visit the art gallery.
13 of the boys choose to visit the science museum.

	Theatre	Art gallery	Science museum	Totals
Girls	11	9		
Boys			13	23
Totals	19		20	50

(a) Copy and complete the table.
(b) How many of the girls choose to visit the science museum?

Edexcel

7 The table shows the results of a survey of 500 people.

	Can drive	Cannot drive
Men	180	20
Women	240	60

A newspaper headline states:

Survey shows that more women can drive than men.

Do the results of the survey support this headline?
Give a reason for your answer.

Presentation of Data 1

What you need to know

- **Pictogram**. Symbols are used to represent information.
  Each symbol can represent one or more items of data.

- **Bar chart**. Used for data which can be counted.
  Often used to compare quantities of data in a distribution.
  The length of each bar represents frequency.
  The longest bar represents the **mode**.
  The difference between the largest and smallest variable
  is called the **range**.

  > Bars can be drawn
  > horizontally or vertically.
  > Bars are the same width and
  > there are gaps between bars.

- **Bar-line graph**. Instead of drawing bars, horizontal or vertical lines are drawn to show frequency.

  Eg 1 The graph shows the number of goals scored by a football team in 10 matches.

  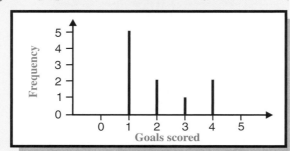

  (a) Which number of goals scored is the mode?
  (b) What is the range of the number of goals scored?

  (a) The tallest bar represents the mode. The mode is 1 goal.
  (b) The range is the difference between the largest and smallest number of goals scored.
  The range = $4 - 1 = 3$

- **Pie chart**. Used for data which can be counted.
  Often used to compare proportions of data, usually with the total.
  The whole circle represents all the data.
  The size of each sector represents the frequency of data in that sector.
  The largest sector represents the **mode**.

  Eg 2 The pie chart shows the makes of 120 cars.
  (a) Which make of car is the mode?
  (b) How many of the cars are Ford?

  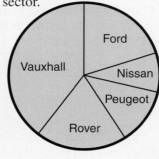

  (a) The sector representing Vauxhall is the largest.
  Therefore, Vauxhall is the mode.
  (b) The angle of the sector representing Ford is 72°.

  The number of Ford cars $= \frac{72}{360} \times 120 = 24$

- **Stem and leaf diagrams**. Used to represent data in its original form. Data is split into two parts.
  The part with the higher place value is the stem.   e.g.   15 = stem 1, leaf 5.
  A key is given to show the value of the data.   e.g.   3|4 means 3.4 etc.
  The data is shown in numerical order on the diagram.   e.g.   2|3 5 9 represents 23, 25, 29.

  Back to back stem and leaf diagrams can be used to compare two sets of data.

  Eg 3 The times, in seconds, taken by 10 students
  to complete a puzzle are shown.

  9 23 17 20 12 11 24 12 10 26

  Construct a stem and leaf diagram
  to represent this information.

  2|0 means 20 seconds

0	9
1	0 1 2 2 7
2	0 3 4 6

1 The pictogram shows the number of parcels posted at the High Street Post Office on Monday, Tuesday and Wednesday.

(a) How many parcels were posted on
   (i) Monday,
   (ii) Tuesday?

25 parcels were posted on Thursday.
(b) Copy and complete the pictogram.

Monday	
Tuesday	
Wednesday	
Thursday	

Represents 20 parcels

Edexcel

2 A sample of retired people was asked, "Which television channel do you watch the most?" The table shows the results.

Television channel	BBC 1	BBC 2	ITV 1	Channel 4	Channel 5
Number of people	16	9	11	10	4

(a) Draw a bar chart to show these results.
(b) What percentage watched Channel 4 the most?

3 Causeway Hockey Club have a hockey team for men and a hockey team for women.
The bar chart shows the number of goals scored in matches played by these teams last season.

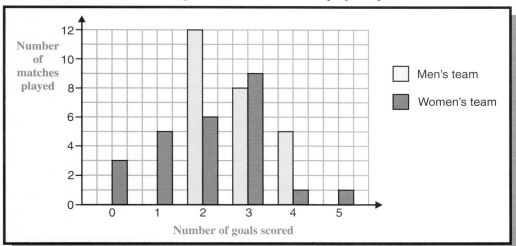

(a) How many matches did each team play?
(b) For the men's team, find the range and mode in the number of goals scored.
(c) Compare and comment on the goals scored by these teams last season.

4 The stem and leaf diagram shows the highest November temperature recorded in 12 European countries last year.

(a) How many countries are included?
(b) What is the maximum temperature recorded?
(c) Which temperature is the mode?
(d) What is the range of these temperatures?

```
                              0 | 7   means 7°C
0 | 7   9
1 | 0   3   4   4   4   7   8
2 | 0   1   2
```

5 40 passengers at Gatwick Airport were asked which country they were flying to.
Here is a frequency table which shows that information.

Country	USA	France	Spain	Greece
Number of passengers	14	10	11	5

Draw an accurate pie chart to show this information.

Edexcel

What you need to know

- There are three types of **average**: the **mode**, the **median** and the **mean**.

Eg 1 The number of text messages received by 7 students on Saturday is shown.

$$2 \quad 4 \quad 3 \quad 4 \quad 4 \quad 3 \quad 2$$

Find   (a) the mode,   (b) the median,   (c) the mean,   (d) the range.

> The **mode** is the most common amount.
>
> The **median** is found by arranging the data in order of size and taking the middle amount (or the mean of the two middle amounts).
>
> The **mean** is found by dividing the total of all the data by the number of data values.
>
> The **range** is a measure of **spread**.
> Range = highest amount − lowest amount

(a) The mode is 4.

(b) 2   2   3   ③   4   4   4

     The median is 3.

(c) The mean $= \dfrac{2 + 4 + 3 + 4 + 4 + 3 + 2}{7}$

$= \dfrac{22}{7} = 3.14\ldots$

$= 3.1$, correct to 1 d.p.

(d) The range $= 4 - 2 = 2$

- To find the mean of a **frequency distribution** use:

$$\text{Mean} = \dfrac{\text{Total of all amounts}}{\text{Number of amounts}}$$

Eg 2 The table shows the number of stamps on some parcels.

Number of stamps	1	2	3	4
Number of parcels	5	6	9	4

Find the mean number of stamps per parcel.

$\text{Mean} = \dfrac{\text{Total number of stamps}}{\text{Number of parcels}}$

$= \dfrac{1 \times 5 + 2 \times 6 + 3 \times 9 + 4 \times 4}{5 + 6 + 9 + 4}$

$= \dfrac{60}{24} = 2.5$

- Choosing the best average to use:

When the most **popular** value is wanted use the **mode**.

When **half** of the values have to be above the average use the **median**.

When a **typical** value is wanted use either the **mode** or the **median**.

When all the **actual** values have to be taken into account use the **mean**.

When the average should not be distorted by a few very small or very large values do **not** use the mean.

Exercise 30   Do not use a calculator for questions 1 to 3.

1   Nine students were asked to estimate the length of this line, correct to the nearest centimetre.

The estimates the students made are shown.

$$8 \quad 10 \quad 10 \quad 10 \quad 11 \quad 12 \quad 12 \quad 14 \quad 15$$

(a) What is the range in their estimates?

(b) Which estimate is the mode?

(c) Which estimate is the median?

(d) Work out the mean of their estimates.

Averages and Range

2 The numbers of goals scored by a netball team in 11 matches were:

15, 12, 17, 9, 12, 23, 16, 14, 12, 13, 16.

(a) Find the mode of the number of goals scored.

(b) Find the median number of goals scored.

Edexcel

3 Nicky recorded the numbers of people getting off her bus at 10 stops.
Here are her results.

2   4   3   6   3   6   3   7   11   8

For these 10 numbers, work out

(a) the mean,   (b) the median,   (c) the range.   *Edexcel*

4 The prices paid for eight different meals at a restaurant are:

£10   £9   £9.50   £12   £20   £11.50   £11   £9

(a) Which price is the mode?   (b) Find the median price.   (c) Calculate the mean price.

(d) Which of these averages best describes the average price paid for a meal?
Give a reason for your answer.

5 (a) The number of hours of sunshine each day last week is shown.

Monday	Tuesday	Wednesday	Thursday	Friday	Saturday	Sunday
5.3	6.4	3.7	4.8	7.5	8.6	5.7

(i) What is the range in the number of hours of sunshine each day?

(ii) Work out the mean number of hours of sunshine each day.

(b) In the same week last year, the range in the number of hours of sunshine each day was
9 hours and the mean was 3.5 hours.
Compare the number of hours of sunshine each day in these two weeks.

6 20 students took part in a competition.
The frequency table shows the points they scored.
Work out the total number of points scored by the 20 students.

Points scored	1	2	3
Frequency	9	4	7

Edexcel

7 Helen and Reg play ten-pin bowling.
The graph shows their scores for the first 10 frames.

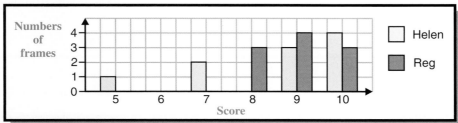

(a) What is the range in the scores for Helen?

(b) Find the mean of the scores for Reg.

(c) Reg says, "My average score is higher than Helen's."
Helen says, "My average score is higher than Reg's."
A friend says, "Your average scores are both the same."
Which average is being used by each person?
Show your working.

8 Darren throws a dice 60 times.
His results are shown.

Score	1	2	3	4	5	6
Frequency	12	10	9	11	10	8

(a) For these results, find

(i) the mode,   (ii) the median,   (iii) the mean.

(b) Darren throws the dice again and scores a 6.
Which of the averages he has found will not change?

- A **time series** is a set of readings taken at time intervals.
- A **line graph** is used to show a time series.

Eg 1 The table shows the temperature of a patient taken every half-hour.

Time	0930	1000	1030	1100	1130	1200
Temperature °C	36.9	37.1	37.6	37.2	36.5	37.0

(a) Draw a line graph to illustrate the data.
(b) Estimate the patient's temperature at 1115.

(a)
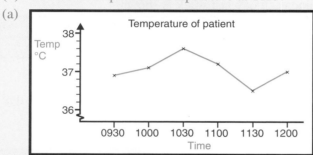

To draw a line graph:
Plot the given values.
Points are joined by lines to show the **trend**.

(b) 36.8°C

Only the plotted points represent **actual values**.
The lines show the **trend** and can be used to **estimate values**.

- **Histogram**. Used to illustrate **grouped frequency distributions.**
  The horizontal axis is a continuous scale.

- **Frequency polygon**. Used to illustrate grouped frequency distributions.
  Often used to compare two or more distributions on the same diagram.
  Frequencies are plotted at the midpoints of the class intervals and joined with straight lines.
  The horizontal axis is a continuous scale.

Eg 2 The frequency distribution of the heights of some boys is shown.

Height (h cm)	$130 \leqslant h < 140$	$140 \leqslant h < 150$	$150 \leqslant h < 160$	$160 \leqslant h < 170$	$170 \leqslant h < 180$
Frequency	1	7	12	9	3

Draw a histogram and a frequency polygon to illustrate the data.

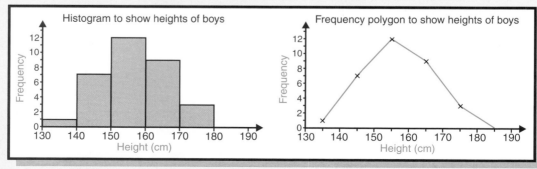

- **Misleading graphs**. Graphs may be misleading if:
  the scales are not labelled,   the scales are not uniform,   the frequency does not begin at zero.

1 On Sunday, Alfie records the outside temperature every two hours.
The temperatures he recorded are shown in the table.

Time of day	0800	1000	1200	1400	1600	1800
Outside temperature (°C)	9	12	15	17	16	14

(a) Draw a line graph to represent the data.
(b) What is the range in the temperatures recorded?
(c) (i) Use your graph to estimate the temperature at 1300.
(ii) Explain why your answer in (c)(i) is an estimate.

2 Robin had a holiday job packing cheese.
Each pack of cheese should weigh 500 grams.
Robin checked the weights, in grams, of 30 packs of cheese. These are the results.

512 506 503 506 499 506 507 499 500 504
502 503 510 508 496 497 497 509 506 496
496 499 497 498 507 511 503 493 498 491

(a) Copy and complete the grouped frequency table for the weights. Use class intervals of 5 g.

Weight (w grams)	Tally	Frequency
$490 \leqslant w < 495$		

(b) Draw a frequency diagram to represent the data.
(c) State the modal class.

Edexcel

3 The table shows the frequency distribution of student absences for a year.

Absences (d days)	Frequency
$0 < d < 5$	4
$5 \leqslant d < 10$	6
$10 \leqslant d < 15$	8
$15 \leqslant d < 20$	5
$20 \leqslant d < 25$	4
$25 \leqslant d < 30$	3

(a) Draw a frequency polygon for this frequency distribution.
(b) What percentage of students were absent for 25 days or more last year?

Edexcel

4 The graph shows the time taken to score the first goal in 20 football matches.

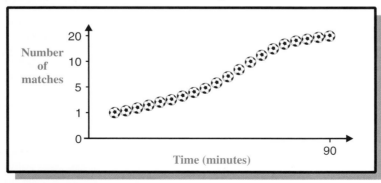

Explain why the graph is misleading.

Scatter Graphs ●●●●●●●●●●

What you need to know

- A **scatter graph** can be used to show the relationship between two sets of data.
- The relationship between two sets of data is referred to as **correlation**.
- You should be able to recognise **positive** and **negative** correlation. The correlation is stronger as points get closer to a straight line.
- When there is a relationship between two sets of data a **line of best fit** can be drawn on the scatter graph.
- The line of best fit can be used to **estimate** the value from one set of the data when the corresponding value of the other set is known.

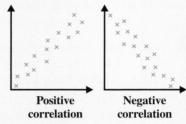

Positive correlation   Negative correlation

Eg 1 The table shows the weights and heights of 10 girls.

Weight (kg)	33	36	37	39	40	42	45	45	48	48
Height (cm)	133	134	137	140	146	146	145	150	152	156

(a) Draw a scatter graph for the data.
(c) What type of correlation is shown?
(b) Describe what the scatter graph shows.
(c) Draw a line of best fit.

Mark a cross on the graph to show the weight and height of each girl.

(a)

Height (cm) vs Weight (kg) scatter graph with points and line of best fit.

(b) The scatter graph shows that taller girls generally weigh more than shorter girls.
(c) Positive correlation.
(d) The line of best fit has been drawn, by eye, on the graph.

On a scatter graph:
The **slope** of the line of best fit shows the **trend** of the data.
The line of best fit does not have to go through the origin of the graph.

Exercise 32

1 The scatter graphs show the results of a survey given to people on holiday at a seaside resort.

Graph A   Graph B   Graph C

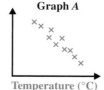

Temperature (°C)   Temperature (°C)   Temperature (°C)

(a) Which scatter graph shows the temperature (°C) plotted against:
  (i) the number of people in the sea,
  (ii) the number of people with coats on,
  (iii) the amount of money people spend?
(b) Which scatter graph shows a positive correlation?

2 The scatter graph shows the results of candidates in two examinations in the same subject.

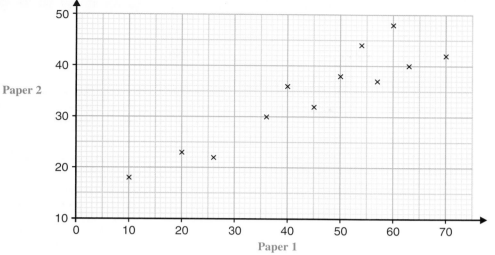

(a) One candidate scored 40 marks on Paper 1.
What mark did this candidate score on Paper 2?
(b) One candidate scored 48 marks on Paper 2.
What mark did this candidate score on Paper 1?
(c) Was the highest mark on both papers scored by the same candidate?
(d) Was the lowest mark on both papers scored by the same candidate?
(e) What type of correlation is there between the marks scored on the two exam papers?

3 Nine different models of car were tested to see how long it took each car to travel 500 metres from a standing start.
The times, together with the size of each engine, are shown in the table.

Engine size cc	1000	1200	1250	1400	1450	1600	1800	1950	2000
Time (seconds)	26	23	23	21	21	19	18	16	14

(a) Use this information to draw a scatter graph.
Label the horizontal axis **Engine size (cc)** from 800 to 2200.
Label the vertical axis **Time (seconds)** from 0 to 26.
(b) Describe the relationship between the time a car takes to travel 500 metres and the size of its engine.
(c) Use your scatter graph to estimate the time taken to travel 500 metres by a car with an engine size of 1700 cc.
Edexcel

4 The table shows the average midday temperature, in °C, and the number of visitors, in thousands, to a country park last year.

Month	Jan	Feb	Mar	Apr	May	Jun	Jul	Aug	Sep	Oct	Nov	Dec
Average midday temperature in °C	3	6	9.5	10.5	12	18	21	23	19	15	8	4
Number of visitors in thousands	6	6	8	11	12	16	20	20	18	13	7	4

(a) Use the information from the table to draw a scatter graph.
(b) Describe the relationship between the average midday temperature and the number of visitors.
(c) (i) Draw a line of best fit on your scatter graph.
(ii) Explain how you can tell the relationship is quite strong.

The average midday temperature for one month next year is forecast to be 14°C.
(d) Use your scatter graph to predict the number of visitors that month, in thousands. *Edexcel*

Probability

What you need to know

- **Probability** describes how likely or unlikely it is that an event will occur.
  Probabilities can be shown on a probability scale.

  Probability **must** be written as a **fraction**, a **decimal** or a **percentage**.

  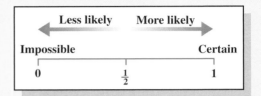

- How to work out probabilities using **equally likely outcomes**.

  $$\text{The probability of an event} = \frac{\text{Number of outcomes in the event}}{\text{Total number of possible outcomes}}$$

  Eg 1 A box contains 7 red pens and 4 blue pens. A pen is taken from the box at random.
  What is the probability that the pen is blue?

  $$P(\text{blue}) = \frac{\text{Number of blue pens}}{\text{Total number of pens}} = \frac{4}{11}$$

  P(blue) stands for the probability that the pen is blue.

- How to use probabilities to **estimate** the number of times an event occurs in an **experiment** or **observation**.

  $$\text{Estimate} = \text{total number of trials (or observations)} \times \text{probability of event}$$

  Eg 2 1000 raffle tickets are sold. Alan buys some tickets.

  The probability that Alan wins first prize is $\frac{1}{50}$.

  How many tickets did Alan buy?   Number of tickets $= 1000 \times \frac{1}{50} = 20$

- **Mutually exclusive events** cannot occur at the same time.

  When A and B are mutually exclusive events: $P(A \text{ or } B) = P(A) + P(B)$

  Eg 3 A box contains red, green, blue and yellow counters.
  The table shows the probability of getting each colour.

Colour	Red	Green	Blue	Yellow
Probability	0.4	0.25	0.25	0.1

  A counter is taken from the box at random.
  What is the probability of getting a red or blue counter?
  P(Red or Blue) = P(Red) + P(Blue) = 0.4 + 0.25 = 0.65

- The probability of an event, A, **not happening** is: $P(\text{not } A) = 1 - P(A)$

  Eg 4 Kathy takes a sweet from a bag at random.
  The probability that it is a toffee is 0.3.
  What is the probability that it is **not** a toffee?
  P(not toffee) = 1 − P(toffee) = 1 − 0.3 = 0.7

- How to find all the possible outcomes when two events are combined.
  By **listing** the outcomes systematically. By using a **possibility space diagram**.

1 Here are three possible events:

A A coin when tossed will come down heads.
B It will snow in August in London.
C There will be a baby born tomorrow.

Which of the three events is
(a) most likely to happen,   (b) least likely to happen?   Edexcel

2 Copy the probability line.

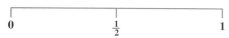

(a) Mark with *H* the probability of getting a head when a fair coin is thrown.
(b) Mark with *S* the probability of getting a 7 when a fair six-sided dice is thrown.
(c) Mark with *N* the probability of getting a number less than 10 when a fair six-sided dice is thrown.   Edexcel

3 A packet contains 1 red balloon, 3 white balloons and 4 blue balloons.
A balloon is taken from the packet at random.
(a) What is the probability that it is red?
(b) What is the probability that it is red or white?
(c) What is the probability that it is not white?

4 A red dice and a blue dice are both numbered 1 to 6.
In a game, both dice are thrown and the total score is found by adding the two numbers.
(a) Copy the table and list all the possible ways in which to score a **total** of 6.

Ways to score a total of 6.	
Number on red dice	**Number on blue dice**

(b) Explain which is more likely, a total score of 6 or a total score of 12.   Edexcel

5 Petra has 5 numbered cards. She uses the cards to do this experiment:

Shuffle the cards and then record the number on the top card.

She repeats the experiment 20 times and gets these results.

3   3   2   3   4   3   5   2   3   4   3   5   3   3   4   2   5   3   4   2

(a) What numbers do you think are on the five cards? Give a reason for your answer.
(b) She repeats the experiment 500 times.
Estimate the number of times she will get a 5. Give a reason for your answer.

6 A letter has a first-class stamp on it.
The probability that the letter will be delivered on the next working day is 0.86.
What is the probability that the letter will **not** be delivered on the next working day?   Edexcel

7 Aimee, Georgina, Hannah and Louisa are the only runners in a race.
The probabilities of Aimee, Georgina, Hannah and Louisa winning the race are shown in the table.

Aimee	Georgina	Hannah	Louisa
0.3	0.2	0.4	

(a) Work out the probability that Louisa will win the race.
(b) Work out the probability that either Aimee or Hannah will win the race.

Section Review - Handling Data

1 The pictogram shows the number of videos hired from a shop each day last week.

Monday	◖◗◖◗ ◖◗
Tuesday	◖◗◖◗ ◖◗◖◗
Wednesday	◖◗◖◗ ◠
Thursday	◖◗◖◗ ◖◗◖◗ ◖◗◠
Friday	◖◗◖◗ ◖◗◖◗ ◖◗◖◗ ◖◗◖◗ ◖◗
Saturday	

On Monday 6 videos were hired.

(a)   How many videos does ◖◗◖◗ represent?

(b)   How many videos were hired on Thursday?

70 videos were hired altogether last week.

(c)   How many videos were hired on Saturday?

2 Paige did a survey about pets. She asked each person, "How many pets do you have?"
Here are her results.

    3   2   1   1   4   2   3   1   0   0   1   3   0
    1   4   2   0   1   5   1   2   4   1   4   2

(a)   Copy and complete the frequency table for this data.

Number of pets	Tally	Frequency
0		
1		

(b)   Draw a bar chart to show this data.

3 The graph shows the results of a traffic survey outside Ashurst School.
The number of each type of vehicle is shown as a percentage of the total number of vehicles seen on the day of the survey.

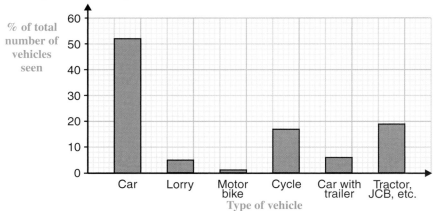

Joe walks outside Ashurst School and records the first vehicle which passes.

(a)   Write **TRUE** or **FALSE** for each of these statements.

    (i)   The vehicle is **most likely** to be a car.

    (ii)   The vehicle is **likely** to be a motorbike.

    (iii)   The vehicle is **unlikely** to be a lorry.

Errol, from Ashurst School, said, "You would get very similar results outside **any** school."

(b)   Explain briefly how you could test whether this statement is true.

Edexcel

4 Here are nine numbers.

7	3	4	9	3	9	3	3	4

Find   (a)   the mode,   (b)   the median,   (c)   the range,   (d)   the mean.   Edexcel

5 Here is a spinner.
The spinner is spun.

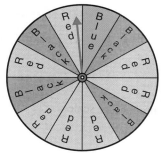

(a)   (i)   Which colour is least likely?
      (ii)   Give a reason for your answer.

(b)   Copy the probability line and mark with an *X* the probability that the colour will be Red.

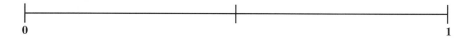

0   1

(c)   Write down the probability that the colour will be Blue.   Edexcel

6 The table shows the number of peas in a sample of pods.

Number of peas	1	2	3	4	5	6	7	8
Number of pods	0	0	2	3	5	7	2	1

(a)   How many pods were in the sample?
(b)   What is the modal number of peas in a pod?
(c)   What is the range in the number of peas in a pod?
(d)   Draw a bar chart to show this information.

7 A railway company wanted to show the
improvements in its train service over 3 years.
This graph was drawn.

Explain why this graph may be misleading.

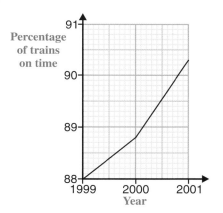

8 Asif has a box of 25 pens.
12 of the pens are blue.   8 of the pens are black.   The rest of the pens are red.
Asif chooses one pen at random from the box.
What is the probability that Asif will choose   (a)   a blue pen,   (b)   a red pen?   Edexcel

9

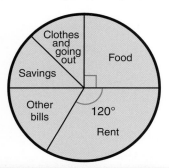

The pie chart shows how Jenny spends her monthly income.
Jenny spends £150 a month on food.

(a)   Work out Jenny's monthly income.

(b)   Work out how much rent Jenny pays each month.

Edexcel

10 The graph shows the distribution of the best height jumped by each girl in a high jump competition.

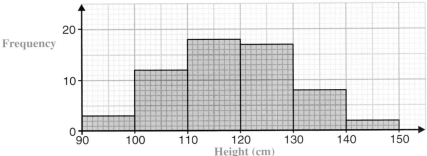

(a) How many girls jumped less than 100 cm?
(b) How many girls jumped between 100 cm and 120 cm?
(c) How many girls took part in the competition?

11 Sylvester did a survey to find the most popular pantomime.
(a) The results for children are shown in the table.

Pantomime	Aladdin	Cinderella	Jack and the Bean Stalk	Peter Pan
Number of children	45	35	25	15

    (i) Draw a clearly labelled pie chart to illustrate this information.
    (ii) Which pantomime is the mode?

(b) The results for adults are shown in the pie chart.
    (i) 20 adults chose Aladdin.
        How many adults were included in the survey?
    (ii) What percentage of adults chose Cinderella?

12 A game is played with two spinners.
You multiply the two numbers on which
the spinners land to get the score.

This score is: $2 \times 4 = 8$

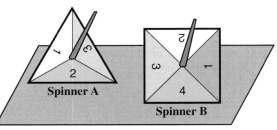

(a) Copy and complete the table to show all the possible scores.
One has been done for you.

×	1	2	3	4
1				
2				8
3				

(b) Work out the probability of getting a score of 6.
(c) Work out the probability of getting a score that is an odd number.

Edexcel

13 The names and prices of four second-hand cars are shown in the table.

Name	Nippy sports	Tuff hatchback	Ace supermini	Mega estate
Price	£12 000	£4000	£6000	£18 000

On the scatter graph, each letter represents one of the cars.

(a) Use the information shown in the table and in the scatter graph to write down the letter which represents each car.

(b) Write down the name of the oldest car.

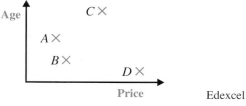

Edexcel

14 The mean of four numbers is 7. The mean of six different numbers is 8.
Calculate the mean of all ten numbers.

15 Grace and Gemma were carrying out a survey on the food people eat in the school canteen.
Grace wrote the question: *"Which foods do you eat?"*
Gemma said that this question was too vague.
Write down two ways in which this question could be improved.

Edexcel

16 The letters of the word **A B B E Y**
are written on separate cards and placed in a box.
A card is taken from the box at random.

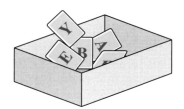

(a) What is the probability that it is the letter **B**?

(b) The probability that it is a vowel is 0.4
What is the probability that it is not a vowel?

17 The lengths of 20 bolts, in centimetres, is shown.

| 7.4 | 5.8 | 4.5 | 5.0 | 6.5 | 6.6 | 7.0 | 5.4 | 4.8 | 6.4 |
| 5.4 | 6.2 | 7.2 | 5.5 | 4.8 | 6.5 | 5.0 | 6.0 | 6.5 | 6.8 |

(a) Draw a stem and leaf diagram to illustrate this information.
(b) What is the range in the lengths of these bolts?
(c) Which length is the median?

18 The table shows information about a group of students.

	Can speak French	Cannot speak French
Male	5	20
Female	12	38

(a) One of these students is chosen at random.
What is the probability that the student can speak French?
(b) Pru says, "If a female student is chosen at random she is more likely to be able to speak French than if a male student is chosen at random." Is she correct?
Explain your answer.

19 Some people were asked how many National Lottery tickets they bought last week.
The results are shown in the table.

Number of tickets	0	1	2	3	4	5	6
Number of people	2	7	5	2	0	3	1

(a) Which number of tickets is the mode?
(b) Work out the median number of tickets.
(c) Find the mean number of tickets.

Edexcel

Exam Practice - Non-calculator Paper

Do not use a calculator for this exercise.

1 6740 people watched a cricket match.
  (a) Write the number 6740 in words.
  (b) Write the number 6740 correct to the nearest hundred.
  (c) Write down the value of the 7 in the number 6740.   Edexcel

2 The table shows the number of books borrowed from a library during five days.

Day	Monday	Tuesday	Wednesday	Thursday	Friday
Number of books	40	35	30	15	50

  (a) How many books were borrowed during these five days?
  (b) Draw a pictogram to represent the information.

   Use  to represent 10 books.

3 Stephen and Edward are playing a game. One player has to describe a sequence of numbers. Then the other player has to write down the first four numbers in the sequence.

Stephen says, "My sequence starts with 2. To get the next number you have to add 5 to the previous number."
  (a) What are the next three numbers Edward should write?

When it is his turn, Edward says, "My sequence starts with 100. To get the next number you have to take away 9 from the previous number."
  (b) What are the next three numbers Stephen should write?   Edexcel

4 (a) Put these numbers in order of size, smallest first.
                    105   30   7   19   2002
  (b) Work out. (i) $105 - 30$ (ii) 19×7 (iii) $2002 \div 7$

5 (a) Copy and shade $\frac{2}{3}$ of this shape.
  (b) Write $\frac{3}{5}$ (i) as a decimal,
                  (ii) as a percentage.
  (c) (i) Write down **thirty-one thousand three hundred and two** in figures.
      (ii) Write down 13 820 to the nearest thousand.
  (d) Explain how you would estimate 97×62.   Edexcel

6 Use these numbers to answer the following questions.

                    3   4   13   27   35   64

  (a) Which number is a factor of 16?   (b) Which number is a multiple of 9?
  (c) Which number is a square number?   (d) Which two numbers add up to 40?

7 Helen is standing at *H*. She is facing North.
She turns anticlockwise through 1 right angle.
  (a) In what direction is she now facing?

Later Harry stands at *H*. He faces South.

He turns clockwise through $1\frac{1}{2}$ right angles.
  (b) In what direction will he then be facing?   Edexcel

8 Nick thinks of a number. He doubles it and then subtracts 3.   The answer is 17.
What is his number?

9 The diagram shows a rectangle and a triangle drawn on 1 cm squared paper.

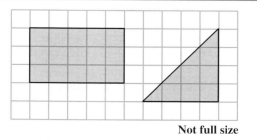

Not full size

(a) How many lines of symmetry has
    (i)   the rectangle,
    (ii) the triangle?
(b) What is the perimeter of the rectangle?
(c) What is the area of the triangle?

10 Copy and complete the shopping bill.

3 bottles of cola at £1.13 per bottle.	£
$2\frac{1}{2}$ kg of potatoes at 30p per kg.	£
Total	£

Edexcel

11 Sports Wear Ltd. hire out ski-suits.
The cost of hiring a ski-suit is calculated using this rule.

> Four pounds per day plus a fixed charge of five pounds.

(a) How much would it cost to hire a ski-suit for 8 days?
(b) Heather paid £65 to hire a ski-suit. For how many days did she hire it?

12 (a) On graph paper plot the points $P(4, 1)$ and $Q(2, -5)$.
    (b) Find the coordinates of the midpoint of the line segment PQ.

13 This is a conversion graph for miles and kilometres.

(a) How many miles are equivalent to 32 kilometres?

(b) How many kilometres are equivalent to 15 miles?

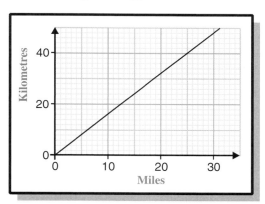

Edexcel

14 Write a rule for finding the next number in each sequence and use your rule to find the next number.
(a) 3, 9, 15, 21, 27, ….   (b) 1, 2, 4, 8, 16, ….

15 A rope is 10 m long. Sean cuts off x metres. What length is left?

16 Here are the numbers of people living in the different houses in a short road.
              4, 2, 3, 4, 5, 1, 3, 2
(a) Work out the mean number of people per house.
(b) Work out the range of the number of people living in a house.

One of the houses is to be chosen at random.

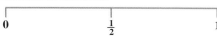

(c) Copy the probability line and mark with the letter X the probability that the house chosen will be the one with 5 people.

Edexcel

17 Use the formula $P = 5m + 2n$ to find the value of P when $m = 4$ and $n = 3$.

18 (a) Draw accurately triangle *PQR* in which *QP* = 5 cm, *PR* = 8 cm and angle *QPR* = 45°.
(b) Measure the length of *QR* on your diagram.
(c) Measure the size of angle *QRP* on your diagram.

19 (a) What fraction of the rectangle is shaded?
Give your answer in its simplest form.
(b) What percentage of the rectangle is **not** shaded?

20 Work out. (a) 563 × 78   (b) 793 ÷ 26   Edexcel

21 Write down the order of rotational symmetry for these shapes.

A   B   C

Edexcel

22 At midday the temperature in Moscow was −6°C.
At midday the temperature in Norwich was 4°C.
(a) How many degrees higher was the temperature in Norwich than the temperature in Moscow?

At midnight the temperature in Norwich had fallen by 7 degrees from 4°C.
(b) Work out the midnight temperature in Norwich.   Edexcel

23 Shreena has a bag of 20 sweets.
10 of the sweets are red. 3 of the sweets are black. The rest of the sweets are white.
Shreena chooses one sweet at random.
What is the probability that Shreena will choose (a) a red sweet, (b) a white sweet?
Edexcel

24 The time it takes to cook a turkey can be found using this rule.

> Allow 40 minutes per kilogram **plus** an extra 20 minutes.

A turkey weighing 4.5 kg is placed in the oven at 9.45 am. At what time will it be cooked?
Give your answer in 12-hour clock time.

25 In the diagram *PQ* and *RS* are straight lines.

(a) (i) Work out the value of *a*.
(ii) Give a reason for your answer.
(b) (i) Work out the value of *b*.
(ii) Give a reason for your answer.
(c) (i) Work out the value of *c*.
(ii) Give a reason for your answer.

Edexcel

26 (a) Work out. (i) 7 − 3.72   (ii) $\frac{3}{5}$ of 9

(b) Find the value of 3*x* + 2*y* when *x* = −4 and *y* = 3.

27 Bruce buys two packets of baby wipes on special offer.
Calculate the actual cost of
each baby wipe.

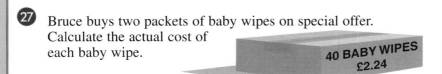

40 BABY WIPES
£2.24

Special Offer
**BUY ONE
GET ONE FREE**

28 (a) Simplify. (i) *a* + 2*a* − 2   (ii) 2*a* × 3*a*   (iii) 5*a* + 3(*b* − *a*)
(b) Solve. (i) 5*x* = −10   (ii) 3*x* − 2 = 10   (iii) 2*x* + 1 = 6

29 The diagram represents the net of a box without a lid.

(a) Calculate the total area of the net.
(b) Calculate the volume of the box.

Edexcel

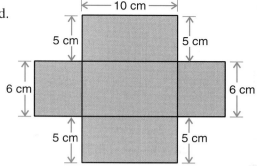

30 Here is a list of ingredients for making some Greek food.

2 cloves of garlic
4 ounces of chick peas
4 tablespoons of olive oil
5 fluid ounces of Tahina paste

These amounts make enough for 6 people.
Change the amounts so that there will be enough for 9 people.

Edexcel

31 (a) In the diagram, angle $BCD = 76°$, $AC = BC$ and ACD is a straight line.
Work out the size of angle BAC.

(b) 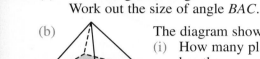 The diagram shows a square-based pyramid.
(i) How many planes of symmetry has the pyramid?
(ii) How many axes of symmetry has the pyramid?

32 (a) Write $\frac{7}{9}$ as a decimal. Give your answer correct to two decimal places.

(b) Write 33%, 0.3, $\frac{8}{25}$ and $\frac{1}{3}$ in order of size, smallest first.

(c) Work out $5^2 + \sqrt{36}$.

33 To calculate the number of mince pies, m, to make for a Christmas Party
for p people, Donna uses the formula $m = 2p + 10$.
(a) How many mince pies would she make for a party of 12 people?
(b) Donna makes 60 mince pies for another party. How many people are expected at this party?

34 Gavin wins £48.
He gives his son one quarter of his winnings. He gives half of the remainder to his wife.
What fraction of his winnings does he keep for himself?

35 Karina is playing a game with these cards.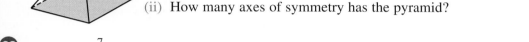

One card is taken at random from the letters.
One card is taken at random from the numbers.
(a) List all the possible outcomes.
(b) Explain why the probability of getting [X] [1] is not $\frac{1}{4}$.

36 Sixty teenagers take part in a dancing competition. The ratio of males to females is 1 : 5.
(a) How many males take part?

After the first round 6 males and 26 females are knocked out.
(b) What is the ratio of males to females left in the competition?
Give your answer in its simplest form.

37 A bag of Estima potatoes weighs 10 kg and costs £1.80.
(a) Estimate the weight of the potatoes in pounds.
(b) King Edward potatoes cost 15% more than Estima potatoes.
What is the cost of a 10 kg bag of King Edward potatoes?

38 (a) Work out the perimeter of this shape.   (b) Work out the area of the triangle.

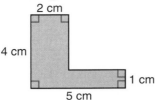

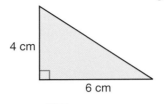

Edexcel

39 In a survey, people going to France were asked:
> ***Where will you be staying on holiday?***

The pie chart shows the results.
(a) What percentage were camping?
(b) 35 people were staying in a caravan.
How many people took part in the survey?

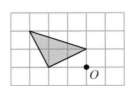

40 A car takes $2\frac{1}{2}$ hours to travel 150 km.

Calculate the average speed of the car in kilometres per hour.

41 (a) Copy the diagram onto squared paper.
Rotate the shape through $180°$ about O.
(b) Make a second copy of the diagram on squared paper.
Enlarge the shape, scale factor 2, centre O.

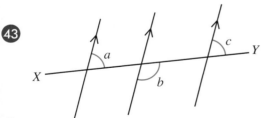

42 (a) Simplify $2x + 5y - 3x + 6y$.
(b) Multiply out $5(x + 3)$.
(c) Find the value of $A = 3t - 1$ when $t = -2$.
(d) Solve the equations   (i) $2(2x + 5) = 34$,   (ii) $5x = 6 + x$.

43

The line XY crosses three parallel lines to form angles a, b and c as shown.
Angle $b = 105°$.
Find the size of angles a and c.

44 A bag contains 50 cubes of which 7 are red. A cube is taken from the bag at random.
(a) The probability that it is white is 0.3.
What is the probability that it is not white?
(b) What is the probability that it is either white or red?

45 The diagram shows a regular hexagon.
Work out   (a) the value of x,   (b) the value of y.

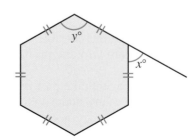

46 A quiz has 40 questions.
(a) Grace gets 65% of the questions right.
How many questions did she get right?
(b) Lenny gets 34 questions right.
What percentage of the questions did he get right?

47 (a) Estimate $\dfrac{53 \times 197}{3.9}$.   (b) Work out $1\frac{1}{4} + \frac{2}{3}$.

48 Draw and label the lines $y = x + 1$ and $x + y = 3$ for values of x from -1 to 3.

Exam Practice - Calculator Paper

You may use a calculator for this exercise.

1   (a)   Which of the numbers 8, −4, 0 or 5 is an odd number?
     (b)   Write the number 3568 to the nearest 10.
     (c)   What is the value of the 4 in the number 3.42?

2   (a)   List these numbers in order, smallest first. | 13   5   −7   0   −1 |
     (b)   What is the difference between the largest number and the smallest number in your list?

3   Copy the diagram and draw a reflection
of the shape in the mirror line PQ.

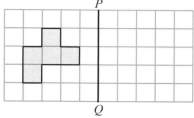

4   The results of a survey of the holiday destinations of people booking holidays abroad are
shown in the bar chart.

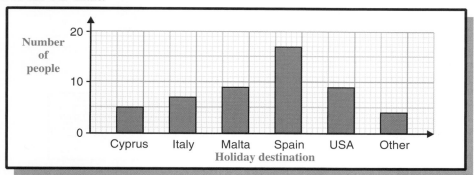

     (a)   Which holiday destination is the mode?
     (b)   How many more people are going to Spain than to Cyprus?
     (c)   How many people are included in the survey?

5   Pic 'n' mix chocolates cost £7 per kilogram. Bernard buys 0.6 kg of chocolates.
     (a)   (i)   How much did the chocolates cost?
           (ii)   He pays with a £10 note. How much change should he get?
     (b)   How many grams is 0.6 kg?

6   Here are some patterns made out of matchsticks.

           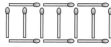

    Pattern number1   **Pattern number 2**   **Pattern number 3**

     (a)   Draw a diagram of Pattern number 4.
     (b)   Copy and complete the table to show the number of matchsticks needed for
           Pattern number 4 and Pattern number 5.

Pattern number	1	2	3	4	5
Number of matchsticks	5	9	13		

     (c)   Work out the pattern number that needs exactly 41 matchsticks.
     (d)   (i)   How many matchsticks are needed for Pattern number 100?
           (ii)   Describe how you found this answer.

Edexcel

7 (a) Which of these triangles are congruent?

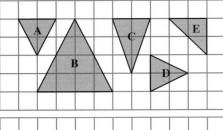

(b) Which of these shapes is a trapezium?

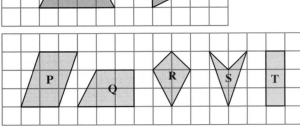

8 Natasha uses this formula to work out her Total pay.

Total pay = Rate per hour × Number of hours + Bonus

Her Rate per hour is £5.50. She works for 35 hours. She has a Bonus of £12.50.
Work out her Total pay.

Edexcel

9 (a) What metric unit of length would you use to measure the length of a large coach?

(b) Using the unit you gave in part (a), estimate the length of a large coach.

Edexcel

10 The times of rail journeys from Guildford to Waterloo are shown.

Guildford	0703	0722	0730	0733	0749	0752
Worplesdon	0708	0727	—	0739	—	0757
Clapham Junction	0752	—	0800	0822	—	—
Waterloo	0800	0815	0808	0830	0823	0844

(a) Karen catches the 0722 from Guildford to Waterloo.
How many minutes does the journey take?

(b) Graham arrives at Worplesdon station at 0715.
What is the time of the next train to Clapham Junction?

11 The diagram shows two gear wheels.
The large wheel has 24 teeth.
The small wheel has 12 teeth.

Describe what happens to the small wheel
when the large wheel is turned through 90° in a clockwise direction.

12 On a musical keyboard there are 5 black keys for every 7 white keys.
The keyboard has 28 white keys. How many black keys does it have?

13 The table has a square top with sides of length 50 cm.

(a) What is the perimeter of the table top?
(b) What is the area of the table top?

14 Work out. (a) $6.25 \times 13 - 6.25 \times 3$ (b) $\frac{10}{25} \times 15$ (c) $3.5^2 - 2.5^2$

15 (a) (i) Calculate $\sqrt{3}$. Give your answer correct to two decimal places.
(ii) Calculate $(0.6)^3$.
(b) What is the value of m, if $47.6 \div m = 0.\dot{3}$?

16 Copy the diagram and draw two more shapes so that the final pattern has rotational symmetry of order 4.

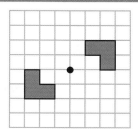

17 Tom Brown was going to America for his holiday.
The bank sold him £450 worth of dollars at a rate of 1.52 dollars to the pound.
(a)   How many dollars did Tom receive?

Tom was unable to go to America.
The bank bought back the dollars at a rate of 1.50 dollars to the pound but charged Tom commission when it bought back the dollars. Tom received £450.
(b)   How much commission, in pounds, did the bank charge?   Edexcel

18 (a)   Simplify $5g - 3g + 2g$.
(b)   Solve the equations   (i) $3n = 12$,   (ii) $3m + 1 = 10$.
(c)   Find the value of $2h^2$ when $h = 3$.

19 On a map the distance between two hospitals is 14.5 cm.
The map has been drawn to a scale of 1 to 250 000.
Calculate the actual distance between the hospitals in kilometres.

20 Show how this kite will tessellate.
You should draw at least 6 kites.

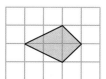

Edexcel

21 Here is an Input-Output diagram.

(a)   What is the Output when the Input is -1?
(b)   What is the Input when the Output is 9?
(c)   When the Input is x, what is the Output in terms of x?

22 Cheri is paid a basic rate of £5.40 per hour for a 35-hour week.

Overtime is paid at $1\frac{1}{2}$ times the basic rate.

Last week she worked 41 hours. Calculate her pay for last week.

23 Calculate the value of: (a) $\dfrac{7.89 + 13.56}{5}$ (b) $2.6^2 - \sqrt{6.2}$

24 Jemma has 4 litres of milk and 20 glasses. Each glass holds one third of a pint.
Can Jemma fill all the glasses? Show your working.

25 A fairground ride is decorated with 240 coloured lights.
(a)   15% of the lights are red. How many red lights are there?
(b)   30 of the 240 lights are not working. What percentage of lights are not working?

26 Jacob is 3.7 kg heavier than Isaac. The sum of their weights is 44.5 kg.
How heavy is Jacob?

27 Write these numbers in order of size. Start with the smallest number.

$$\frac{7}{8} \qquad 80\% \qquad 0.9 \qquad \frac{8}{9}$$

Edexcel

28

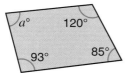

SOUP SPECIALS
Choose from: Chicken, Mushroom, Tomato or Vegetable

The table shows the number of people choosing each soup at lunchtime.

Soup	Chicken	Mushroom	Tomato	Vegetable
Number of people	16	8	10	14

Draw a clearly labelled pie chart to represent this information.

29 A rowing boat has 8 oarsmen and a cox. The mean weight of the oarsmen is 73.2 kg.
When the cox is included the mean weight is 71.6 kg. Calculate the weight of the cox.

30 The diagrams show a quadrilateral, a regular hexagon and a regular octagon.
Work out the size of the angles marked $a°$, $b°$ and $c°$.

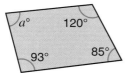
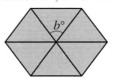
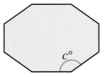

Not drawn accurately

Edexcel

31 The stem and leaf diagram shows the weights,
in grams, of letters posted by a secretary.

(a) How many letters were posted?
(b) What is the median weight of one of these letters?
(c) What is the range in the weights of these letters?
(d) Calculate the mean weight of a letter?

```
              1|5  means 15 grams
1 |  5   8
2 |  0   4   5   6   8   8
3 |  1   2   3   5   7
4 |  2   5
```

32

Gravy
Granules
180 g
Normal price
54p

Gravy
Granules
300 g
Normal price
90p

The diagram shows the weights and prices of
two packets of gravy granules.
This week both packets are on special offer.
The smaller packet has one third off the normal price.
The larger packet has 30% off the normal price.
Which packet is better value this week?
Show your working.

33 (a) A dinner plate has a diameter of 18 cm. Calculate the circumference of the dinner plate.
(b) A tea plate has a radius of 8 cm. Calculate the area of the tea plate.

34 Work out $\frac{2}{5} - \frac{1}{3}$, giving your answer as a fraction.

35 This rule is used to find out how far apart to plant two bushes.

Add the heights of the bushes. Divide your answer by 3.

Ben is going to plant two different bushes.
He should plant them 50 cm apart.
The height of one of the bushes is 90 cm.
(a) Work out the height of the other bush.

The heights of two different bushes are a cm and b cm.
The two bushes should be planted d cm apart.
(b) Write down a formula for d in terms of a and b.

Edexcel

36 Work out 45% of £24.

Edexcel

37 There are 2.54 centimetres in 1 inch. There are 12 inches in 1 foot. There are 3 feet in 1 yard.
(a) Calculate the number of yards in 10 metres.
(b) Calculate the number of metres in 10 yards.

Edexcel

38 Work out the area of the shape.

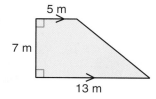

Edexcel

39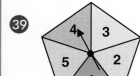

John has a spinner in the shape of a regular pentagon.
Scores of 1, 2, 3, 4, 5 are equally likely when the spinner is spun.
John spins the spinner 200 times and records the scores.
Approximately how many times will he score an even number?   *Edexcel*

40 Bob cycles from home to work.
The travel graph shows his journey.

(a) On his way to work Bob stopped
    to buy a newspaper.
    At what time did he stop?

(b) (i) During which part of his journey
        did Bob cycle fastest?
        Give a reason for your answer.
    (ii) Calculate his average speed in
         kilometres per hour for this part
         of his journey.

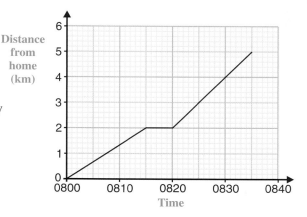

41 A hang glider flies 2.8 km on a bearing of 070° from *P* to *Q* and then 2 km on a bearing of
200° from *Q* to *R*.
(a) Make a scale drawing to show the flight of the hang glider from *P* to *Q* to *R*.
    Use a scale of 1 cm to 200 m.
(b) From *R* the hang glider flies directly back to *P*.
    Use your drawing to find the distance and bearing of *P* from *R*.

42 A regular polygon has 9 sides.
Work out the sum of its interior angles.

43 Solve the equations.   (a) $3y + 7 = 28$ (b) $2(3p + 2) = 19$ (c) $3t - 4 = 5t - 10$
Edexcel

44 The table shows the birth rate and the life expectancy for 12 countries.

Birth rate	13	17	21	25	28	30	31	34	38	41	44	47
Life expectancy (years)	75	73	71	68	65	62	61	65	61	56	51	49

(a) Plot the information as a scatter graph.
(b) Describe the relationship between the birth rate and the life expectancy.
(c) Draw a line of best fit on your scatter graph.

The birth rate in a country is 42.
(d) Use your scatter graph to estimate the life expectancy in that country.   *Edexcel*

45 The perimeter of the pentagon is 200 cm.
Work out the value of *x*.

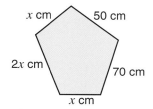

Edexcel

Answers

SECTION 1

Exercise 1   Page 1

1. 605 230

2. 117, 100, 85, 23, 9

3. (a) 3 thousands
   (b) Twenty-three thousand five hundred and forty-seven

4. 93 pence

5. (a) 81
   (b) (i) 35   (ii) 100   (iii) 10

6. (a) 1005   (b) 191   (c) 183

7.

	100 g	200 g	300 g	Total
Ground	15	50	55	120
Powder	80	35	26	141
Granules	40	45	54	139
Total	135	130	135	400

8. (a) (i) 2358   (ii) 8532   (b) 6174

9. (a) 466 km   (b) Jean's journey by 34 km.

10. (a) 12 000   (b) 500   (c) 175   (d) 15

11. £8.64

12. £181 per month

13. 50 boxes

14. £6894

SECTION 2

Exercise 2   Page 2

1. (a) 18   (b) 12   (c) 8

2. (a) 626   (b) 630   (c) 600

3. 8700

4. 19 500

5. 300 km + 100 km = 400 km

6. $\dfrac{3000 \times 40}{100} = £1200$

7. (a) 15 ÷ 3   (b) 5 pairs

8. 2000 ÷ 40 = 50

9. (a) 40 × 90   (b) 3600   (c) 49

10. (a) 100 is bigger than 97, **and**
        50 is bigger than 49.
    (b) Smaller.
        1000 is smaller than 1067, **and**
        50 is bigger than 48.

11. (a) 20 × 70 = 1400 seats
    (b) 1400 × £10 = £14 000

12. 5 tickets

13. 17 boxes

14. $\dfrac{400 + 200}{40} = \dfrac{600}{40} = 15$
    Answer is wrong.

15. (a) $\dfrac{20 \times 60}{100} = \dfrac{1200}{100} = 12$
    (b) 12 − 10.875 = 1.125

16. (a) $\dfrac{9000}{10} \times 70p = £630$
    (b) 9000 is bigger than 8873,
        10 is smaller than 11, **and**
        70 is bigger than 69.9.

SECTION 3

Exercise 3   Page 5

1. (a) 23.0
   (b) 0.065
   (c) 0.065, 0.9, 4.5, 13.5, 23.0
   (d) 0.065 and 0.9

2. (a) 18.59   (b) 11.37
   (c) 2.9   (d) 2.7

3. 4.9 kg

4. £26.97

5. £1.69

6. (a) 320   (b) 0.32

7. (a) 560. E.g. divide by 10, multiply by 8.
   (b) 150. E.g. multiply by 10, divide by 4.

8. (a) 3.2 × 8.5
   (b) No.   3.2 × 8.5 = 27.2

9. (a) (i) 4.02   (ii) 12
   (b) (i) 136   (ii) 0.0245

10. (a) 7.36   (b) 3.2   (c) 230

11. 32 pence

12. (a) $\dfrac{3}{10}$ (b) $\dfrac{3}{100}$ (c) $\dfrac{33}{100}$

13. 40 minutes

14. 1.57 m

15. 11.5 p/kg.   Bag: 38 p/kg,   sack: 26.5 p/kg.

16. (a) 14.95   (b) 15.0

17. £3.61

SECTION 4

Exercise 4   Page 7

1. (a) 12, 20, 24, 30, 100
   (b) 20, 30, 100
   (c) 24 is double 12

2. (a) 5, 11, 17   (b) 2, 5   (c) 20

3. (a) 35   (b) 1, 2, 3, 6, 9, 18
   (c) 1, 2, 3, 6

4. 12

5. (a) 16   (b) 9   (c) 8

6. (a) 5   (b) 64

7. (a) 36, 64   (b) 64   (c) 11

8. (a) 72   (b) 17   (c) 112

9. (a) $\sqrt{225}$, $\sqrt{225} = 15$, $3^3 = 27$
   (b) 0.25

10. (a) 8 and 9   (b) 8.37

11. (a) 0.14   (b) 31.36

12. 45.02

13. (a) 18.277415…   (b) 18.28

14. (a) 125
    (b) (i) 4.48608961…   (ii) 4.49

SECTION 5

Exercise 5   Page 8

1. (a) $-3°C$ (b) $-13°C$

2. (a) Oslo   (b) Warsaw

3. 140 m

4. -9, -3, 0, 5, 7, 17

5. (a) 5   (b) -15 (c) -50 (d) -2

6. (a) 6   (b) 5   (c) -3

7. (a) London   (b) 4°C
   (c) Aberdeen   (d) Cardiff

8. £57 overdrawn ($-$£57)

9. (a) 6 degrees   (b) Between 1200 and 1800

10. (a) (i) 7°C   (ii) 6°C
    (b) 2°C   (c) $-15°C$

11. (a) 4   (b) 11   (c) -3

12. 7 degrees

13. 20°F

14. 5

SECTION 6

Exercise 6   Page 10

1. (a) $\frac{2}{5}$ (b) Shade 4 parts.

2. (a) $n = 9$ (b) $n = 2$ (c) $n = 20$

3. $\frac{3}{9}$ and $\frac{7}{35}$

4. (a) $\frac{7}{10}$ as $\frac{4}{5} = \frac{8}{10}$ (b) $\frac{5}{12}$

5. $\frac{1}{4}$, $\frac{7}{20}$, $\frac{3}{8}$, $\frac{2}{5}$

6. £8

7. 15 miles

8. 8

9. $\frac{2}{3}$

10. £46

11. £3.14

12. $\frac{1}{5}$

13. (a) $2\frac{1}{10}$ (b) $\frac{1}{8}$ (c) 16
    (d) $\frac{3}{8}$ (e) $\frac{2}{5}$

14. (a) 0.25   (b) 0.7   (c) 0.6   (d) 0.125

15. 2.4

16. $\frac{4}{15}$

17. $\frac{1}{10}$

18. £2.80 per kilogram

SECTION 7

Exercise 7   Page 12

1. (a) 30%   (b) 25%   (c) 40%

2. 0.02, 20%, $\frac{1}{2}$

3. (a) 2 pence   (b) 15 kg   (c) £45

4. Daisy.   Daisy scored $\frac{4}{5}$ = 80%.

5.

Fraction	$\frac{3}{4}$	$\frac{3}{10}$	$\frac{3}{5}$
Decimal	0.75	0.3	0.6
Percentage	75%	30%	60%

6. 125 people

7. 700 people

8. £13.50

9. 60 pence

10. (a) 20%   (b) 25%

11. 5%

12. 60%

13. (a) 126   (b) 30%

14. £72

15. £8.45 per hour

16. £31.35

17. £4.56

18. 25%

19. 15%

20. 46%

SECTION 8

Exercise 8   Page 14

1. (a) £5.75   (b) 9 minutes

2. (a) 0715   (b) 32 minutes   (c) 0623

3. (a) 64 euros (b) £6.25

4. 12 days

5. £213.75

6. Small bar.   Large: 2.66 g/p,   small: 2.78 g/p

7. £480

8. Washing Power: £247.50
Whytes: £256.00
Clean Up: £246.75

SECTION 9

Exercise 9   Page16

1. £13

2. £1376.25

3. £207.40

4. £29.90

5. £7 × 30 = £210

6. (a) £1892   (b) £189.20

7. £5.60

8. (a) £7.40   (b) £155.40

9. £209.25

10. £132.50

11. (a) (i) £12.60   (ii) £151.20
(b) 59 years old
(c) 15%

12. 4 hours

13. £1746.30

14. £40.45

SECTION 10

Exercise 10   Page 18

1. (a) 1 : 3   (b) 2 : 1   (c) 2 : 3

2. 3 cm by 4 cm

3. 8 large bricks

4. 4 cm

5. 7.5 kg

6. £150

7. (a) $\frac{1}{4}$ (b) 75%

8. 150 g butter, 120 g sugar, 135 g flour, 3 eggs,
45 ml milk.

9. (a) 70%   (b) 9 women

10. £44.75

11. £123.75

12. 840 males

13. 20

14. 4 : 1

15. 1 : 20 000

Section Review   Page 20

1. (a) 45 608   (b) 46 000

2. (a) (i) 6, 10, 16, 61, 100
(ii) 193
(b) (i) 63   (ii) 2000   (iii) 25

3. (a) 75%   (b) 25%

4. (a) 16 pence   (b) £1.88

5. 424 km

6. 7 hours 47 minutes

7. One million

8. (a) 2, 8, 12, 14, 16
    (b) 3, 9, 12
    (c) 3 is the square root of 9,
        5 is the square root of 25.

9. (a) 49 pence   (b) £4.20

10. £4752

11. $\frac{7}{8}$, 0.8, $\frac{3}{4}$, 70%

12. 1500 m

13. (a) 5   (b) £787.50

14. (a) 24, 48   (b) 3, 6
    (c) 9, 64   (d) 8, 64

15. £30

16. (a) $\frac{8}{10} = \frac{4}{5}$
    (b) (i) 57.4   (ii) 57.42
    (c) 49

17. 12 footballs

18. (a) £1.50   (b) £10.91

19. (a) 4.95 m
    (b) 4.95 m, 5.02 m, 5.10 m, 5.15 m, 5.20 m

20. 68 kg

21. (a) 8100   (b) 36 000

22. (a) £144   (b) £7.20
    (c) 3 hours

23. £21

24. (a) (i) 3 tens, 30
        (ii) 3 thousands, 3000
    (b) (i) 2   (ii) 2
    (c) (i) 4384   (ii) 36

25. (a) 800 ÷ 20   (b) 40

26. (a) 0900   (b) 44 minutes

27. (a) 9472   (b) 25

28. (a) −4°C, −2°C, −1°C, 0°C, 1°C,
       3°C, 7°C.
    (b) 11°C

29. (a) −0.4, −0.35, 0.345, 0.35, 0.355
    (b) 0.45
    (c) (i) 4.74   (ii) 0.08   (iii) 80
    (d) £15.60

30. (a) (i) 100 000 (ii) 92
        (iii) 72   (iv) 0.9
    (b) 5^2. $5^2 = 5 \times 5 = 25$,
                $3^3 = 3 \times 3 \times 3 = 27$
    (c) 40

31. (a) (i) 890 km (ii) 551.8 miles
    (b) £11

32. (a) $\frac{1}{2}$, $\frac{3}{5}$, $\frac{5}{8}$, $\frac{2}{3}$, $\frac{3}{4}$
    (b) $\frac{9}{40}$
    (c) (i) $\frac{13}{20}$ (ii) $\frac{1}{6}$ (iii) $\frac{2}{5}$
    (d) $4\frac{4}{5}$ or 4.8

33. (a) 0.65   (b) 65%

34. (a) (i) 777.6   (ii) 1.35
    (b) 80 000

35. (a) 0.7   (b) $\frac{3}{10}$
    (c) 7 : 3

36. (a) $4 \times 5 \times 30 = 600$
    (b) 10 times too big.

37. 1805 dollars

38. 45 pence

39. Disco's: £24
    Bob's: £25.50
    Sanjay's: £25.85

40. 5 litres

41. (a) 474 units (b) £39.73

42. France.   England: $\frac{454}{89} = 5.1$ g/p
            France: $\frac{681}{184} \times 1.58 = 5.8$ g/p

43. 0.208569…

44. (a) 4   (b) 6.65

45. 12.5%

SECTION 11

Exercise 11   Page 24

1. £9k

2. $t + 5$ years

3. $3x + 2y$ pence

4. $4x + 200$ degrees

5. $5d + 15$ pence

6. (a) $7x$ (b) $7y - 5$

7.

$a + a$	and	$2a$
$2(a + 1)$	and	$2a + 2$
$2a + 1$	and	$a + a + 1$
a^2	and	$a \times a$

8. (a) (i) $3x + 3$ (ii) $x + 2y$
    (b) (i) $2x + 6$ (ii) $x^2 - x$
    (c) (i) $2x - 5$ (ii) $13 + 3x$
    (d) (i) $2(a - 3)$ (ii) $x(x + 2)$

9. (a) (i) $3x$ (ii) $3a + 2b$ (iii) $3a + 6$
    (b) $8x + 1$

SECTION 12

Exercise 12   Page 25

1. (a) 15   (b) 9
    (c) 5   (d) 4

2. (a) $x = 5$ (b) $x = 2$
    (c) $x = 7$ (d) $x = 3$

3. 6

4.

Input	3	5	-2
Output	9	13	-1

5. (a) 5   (b) 4

6. (a) $x = 10$ (b) $x = 5$
    (c) $x = 4$ (d) $x = -6$

7. (a) $x = -1$ (b) $x = \frac{1}{2}$
    (c) $x = 5\frac{1}{2}$ (d) $x = -0.8$

SECTION 13

Exercise 13   Page 26

1. (a) $x = 11$ (b) $x = 6$

2. (a) $x = 8$ (b) $x = 1$
    (c) $x = -4$ (d) $x = 2.5$

3. (a) $p = 5$ (b) $q = -1$
    (c) $r = -1\frac{1}{2}$

4. (a) $x = -1.5$ (b) $x = 2.5$
    (c) $x = 0.6$ (d) $x = 1.5$

5. (a) $t = 5$ (b) $x = 3\frac{1}{2}$
    (c) $y = -6$

6. (a) $n + (n + 3) + (2n - 1) = 4n + 2$
    (b) $4n + 2 = 30$
          $n = 7$

7. $n + (2n + 5) = 47$
      $3n + 5 = 47$
         $n = 14$
Larger box has 33 chocolates.

8. $x = 5$

SECTION 14

Exercise 14   Page 27

1. 4

2. -1

3. $P = 40$

4. $H = -13$

5. $C = 65n$

6. $L = -10$

7. $A = -11$

8. 90

9. (a) £1.05   (b) £1.26

10. (a) 40 km   (b) $K = \dfrac{8M}{5}$
     (c) $M = 37.5$

SECTION 15

Exercise 15   Page 28

1. (a) 21, 25   (b) 30, 26

2. (a)

Pattern number 4

    (b)

Pattern number	1	2	3	4	5	6	7
Number of sticks	3	5	7	9	11	13	15

    (c) (i) 31
       (ii) Double the Pattern number and add 1.

3. (a)

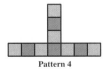

Pattern 4

    (b) 13
       Pattern increases by 3 squares each time.
    (c) 55

4. (a) 17   (b) 81   (c) $\frac{1}{16}$

5. (a) (i) 30
       (ii) Add 6 to the 4th term.
    (b) Term 12

6. (a) 14
    (b) No.
       Number must be (multiple of 3) $- 1$.

7. 5, 6, $5\frac{1}{2}$

8. (a) Multiply the last term by 3.
(b) 405

9. (a)

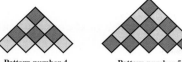

Pattern number 4   Pattern number 5

(b)

Pattern number	1	2	3	4	5	6	7
Number of tiles	1	3	6	10	15	21	28

(c) (i) 78
(ii) Keep adding the next counting number to the last term:
$$1 + \mathbf{2} = 3$$
$$3 + \mathbf{3} = 6$$
$$6 + \mathbf{4} = 10$$
$$\ldots$$
$$66 + \mathbf{12} = 78$$

10. 37, 60

11. No. The sequence does not end.
Sequence: 1, 6, 10, 8, 4, 8, 8, 0, 16, …

12. (a) -3, 0, 5
(b) Yes. When $n = 8$, $8^2 - 4 = 60$.

SECTION 16

Exercise 16   Page 30

1. (a) $P(1, 3)$, $Q(7, 1)$
(b) $(4, 2)$

2. (a) $R(-6, 2)$, $S(3, -4)$
(b) $T(-3, 0)$

3. (a)

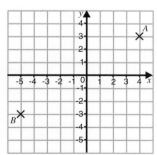

(b) $p = -2$

4. (a)

(b) $(5, 2)$

5. (a) $y = -1$ (b) $x = -3$
(c) $y = x$

6. (a)

x	-1	0	1	2	3
$y = 3x - 2$	-5	-2	1	4	7

(b)

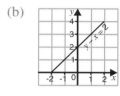

(c) $(0, -2)$

7. (a)

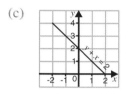

(b)

(c)

(d)

8.

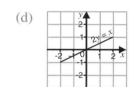

9. (a)

x	-2	0	4
y	-6	-3	3

(b)

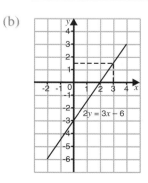

(c) $x = 3$

93

10. (a)

x	0	-5	5
y	2	0	4

(b)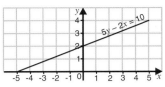

(c) $y = 1.2$

Exercise 17 — Page 32

1. (a) 31 miles
(b) 43 km
(c) Use the graph to convert 100 km to miles and multiply the result by 100.
10 000 km is about 6200 miles.

2. (a) 1306 (b) 1000 and 1100
(c) 50 km/h

3. (a) 30 minutes (b) 18 km
(c) 36 km/h

4. (a)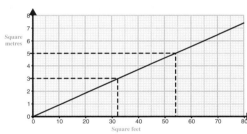

(b) (i) 54 square feet
(ii) 3 square metres

5. (a) 8°C (b) 30 minutes
(c) 30 minutes

Section Review — Page 34

1. (a) $A(2, 1)$ (b)

2. (a) 8 (b) Not an even number.
3. (a) 48 (b) 7
4. 26 points
5. (a)

(b)

Pattern number	1	2	3	4
Number of sides	5	8	11	14

(c) 17 sides (d) 35 sides

6. 21
7. (a) £19.20 (b) £54.20
8. (a) (i) 22
(ii) Add the next counting number, 6.
(b) 12
9. (a) $3x$ pence (b) $x + 30$ pence
10. (a)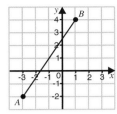

(b) $(-1, 1)$
11. (a) $5t$ pence (b) $t + 5$ pence
12. (a) $x = 10$ (b) $x = 2$
(c) $x = 3$
13. 7
14. (a) (i) 30
(ii) 50th term is an odd number.
All even terms are odd numbers.
(b) Add 4 to the last term.
15. (a) Could be even or odd.
(b) Always odd.
16. (a) $5x$ (b) $3a - 4b$
(c) $3m^2$
17. $P = 20$
18. (a) £$(t - 3)$ (b) £$25x$
19. (a) (i) 17 dollars
(ii) 35 euros
(b) From the graph, 20 euros = 17 dollars.
Multiply by 5 to get,
100 euros = 85 dollars.
20. (a) 6 spoonfuls (b) 600 ml
21. $3x + 5y$ pence
22. (a)

x	-3	-2	-1	0	1	2	3
$y = 3x - 1$	-10	-7	-4	-1	2	5	8

(c) $x = 2.5$

23.

$3a$	and	$2a + a$
$2(a - 1)$	and	$2a - 2$

24. (a) $g = 8$ (b) $a = 5$
(c) $x = 6$ (d) $x = 3$
25. (a) $C = 4u$ (b) $u = 7$
26. (a) 7 (b) $m = 3$
(c) $P = 45$
27. 7
28. (a) $\frac{1}{2}$ (b) -1

29. (a) -5 (b) $2x - 3$

30. £145.50

31. (b) $P(-5, -9)$

32. (a) $x = 4$ (b) $g = 3$
     (c) $y = \dfrac{1}{2}$ (d) $y = -1$

33. 24

34. (a) (i) 5 km   (ii) 11.20 am
        (iii) 10 minutes
     (b) 12 km/h

35. (a) (i) $4c$ (ii) $4r - p$
     (b) (i) 27   (ii) 16

36. (a) (i) $a = 3.5$ (ii) $t = -1$
     (b) $x + x - 3 + x + 7 = 25$
                 $3x + 4 = 25$
                      $x = 7$

37. (a) $p = 5$ (b) $q = -\dfrac{1}{2}$
     (c) $y = \dfrac{1}{4}$

38. (a) 11 pounds   (b) $L = \dfrac{22K}{10}$
     (c) $K = 25$

39. (a) (i) $3(a - 2)$ (ii) $k(k - 2)$
     (b) (i) $5x + 15$ (ii) $m^2 - 4m$
     (c) (i) $x = -1$ (ii) $x = \dfrac{1}{2}$

40. (a)

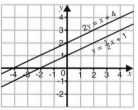

     (b) Lines are parallel.

41. (a) $80x$ pence   (b) $80r + 60t$ pence
     (c) (i) $80g + 120 = 1080$
        (ii) $g = 12$

SECTION 18

Exercise 18   Page 39

1. (a) CD and EF
     (b) AB and CD
     (c) (i) $y = 135°$ (ii) obtuse angle

2. (a) $\angle ABC = 135°$
     (b)

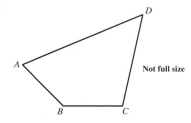

Not full size

3. (a) $a = 143°$ (b) $b = 135°$
     (c) $c = 48°$, $d = 44°$

4. (a) (i) $p = 55°$
        (ii) Vertically opposite angles.
     (b) (i) $q = 125°$
        (ii) p and q are supplementary angles.

5. (a) $\angle PQR = 47°$ (alternate angles)
     (b) $\angle RQS = 68°$

6. $a = 68°$ (supplementary angles)
    $b = 112°$ (corresponding angles)
    $c = 106°$ (allied angles)

7. (a) $a = 117°$, $b = 117°$
     (b) $c = 42°$, $d = 76°$, $e = 62°$
     (c) $f = 51°$

SECTION 19

Exercise 19   Page 40

1. (a) $a = 27°$ (b) $b = 97°$
     (c) $c = 125°$

2. (a) $e = 42°$ (b) $f = 69°$

3. $x = 130°$ ΔPQR is isosceles, $\angle PQR = \angle PRQ$

4. (a) (i) $x = 75°$
        (ii) Corres. $\angle$'s, $\angle BDE$
     (b) (i) $y = 50°$
        (ii) $55° + 75° + y° = 180°$

5. (a) $x = 64°$ (b) $y = 122°$

7. (a) 9 cm²   (b) 10 cm²
     (c) 13.5 cm²

8. (b) (i) $x = 37°$ (ii) acute angle
     (c) 21.66 cm²

9. 14 cm²

SECTION 20

Exercise 20   Page 43

1. (a)

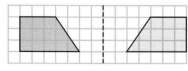

     (b)

2. (a) **A**, **E**   (b) **N**   (c) **O**

3. (a) (i) 3   (ii) 3   (b) (i) 0   (ii) 1
     (c) (i) 0   (ii) 4   (d) (i) 1   (ii) 1

4.

5.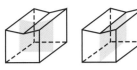

6. **A** and **F**

7. **B** and **D** (SAS)

SECTION **21**

Exercise 21   **Page 45**

1. (a) 14 cm²

(b) (i)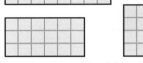

(ii) 8 cm², 18 cm², 20 cm²

2. (a) Square, rhombus
(b) Trapezium
(c) Parallelogram, rhombus

3. (a) $a = 70°$ (b) $b = 132°$
(c) $c = 110°$, $d = 120°$

4. (a) (i) $x = 78°$
(ii) Supplementary angles
(b) (i) $y = 130°$
(ii) Sum of angles in a quad = 360°

5. (a) Kite   (b) $\angle ABC = 114°$

7. (a) 30 cm   (b) 55.04 cm²

8. 24 cm²

9. (a) $x = 51°$ (b) 40 cm²

SECTION **22**

Exercise 22   **Page 46**

1. (a) $a = 53°$ (b) $b = 115°$
(c) $c = 140°$

2. (a) Shape A has rotational symmetry of
             order 6 and 6 lines of symmetry.
          Shape B has rotational symmetry of
             order 2 and 2 lines of symmetry.

(b)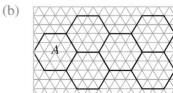

3. (a) $a = 120°$ (b) $b = 60°$, $c = 120°$
(c) $d = 72°$, $e = 108°$

4. (a) Equilateral
(b) (i) $x = 60°$ (ii) $y = 120°$
(c) (i) Rhombus
(ii)

5. 15 sides

6. (a) $\angle ABC = 144°$ (b) $\angle XCY = 108°$

7. A hexagon can be divided
into 4 triangles, as shown.

Sum of the interior angles in a triangle = 180°.
Sum of interior angles of a hexagon is
$4 \times 180° = 720°$.

8. Number of sides $= \dfrac{360°}{30°} = 12$
Sum of interior angles = 1800°

SECTION **23**

Exercise 23   **Page 48**

1. South-East

2. (a) East   (b) North-West
(c) South-East

3. 26 cm

4. 110°

5. (a) (i) 124°   (ii) 304°
(b) 6.25 km

7. (b) (i) 250°   (ii) 1530 m

SECTION **24**

Exercise 24   **Page 50**

1. (a) $C = \pi d = 3 \times 10 = 30$ m
(b) $A = \pi r^2 = 3 \times 5 \times 5 = 75$ m²

2. (a) 15.7 cm   (b) 19.6 cm²

3. 6360 cm²

4. 201 cm

5. 754 cm²

6. 19.9 times

7. 81.7 m²

8. 1050 cm²

9. 106 revolutions

10. (a) 707 cm²
(b) (i) 30   (ii) 8794 cm²

SECTION 25

Exercise 25 — Page 53

1. (a) 5 faces, 8 edges, 5 vertices
   (b) **R**

2. (a) (b)

3. (a) 22 cm (b) 11 cm²
   (c)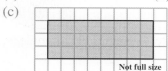
   Not full size

4. 37 m²

5. (a) 30 cubes
   (b) (i)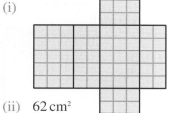

   (ii) 62 cm²

6. (a) 24 m³ (b) 68 m²

SECTION 26

Exercise 26 — Page 55

1. (a)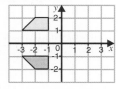

   (b)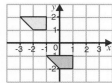

   (c)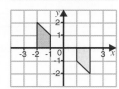

2. (a) Rotation, 90° anticlockwise, about (0, 0).
   (b) Translation 4 units to the right and 3 units down.
   (c) Enlargement, scale factor 3, centre (0, 0).

3.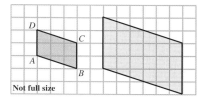
   Not full size

4.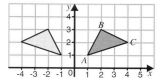

5.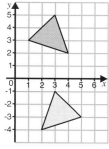

6. (a) $x = -1$
   (b) One unit to the left and 2 units up.
   (c)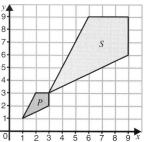

SECTION 27

Exercise 27 — Page 57

1. (a) 15 grams (b) 3.28 kg
   (c) 44 km/h

2. (a) Metres (b) Litres
   (c) Square metres (d) Grams

3. 14 m

4. (a) 6 km (b) 60 g
   (c) 60 cm² (d) 60 m³

5. 1.8 m²

6. (a) 64 km (b) 25 miles

7. 54 litres

8. 1 kg pot.   1 kg pot: $\frac{1000}{150} = 6.6\ldots$ g/p

   1 lb pot: $\frac{1 \times 1000}{2.2 \times 71} = 6.4\ldots$ g/p

9. Debbie is taller.   5 ft 4 in = 160 cm
   Joyce is heavier.   9 st 2 lb = 58.2 kg

10. 64 km/h

11. $1\frac{1}{2}$ hours

12. 165 km

13. 40 miles per hour

Section Review   Page 58

1. (a) (i) (4, 6)   (ii) (4, 1)
  (b) *AD* and *BC*
  (c) (i) Angle *B* = 122°
    (ii) Obtuse angle

2. (a) 12   (b) 5
  (c) cone

3. (a) 17 cm²   (b) 24 cm

4. (a) East   (b) South-West

5. (a) 8000 g and 8 kg   (b) 0.2 km
  (c) 1.4 kg

6. (a) 12 cm³
  (b) (i) 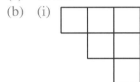   (ii)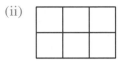

7.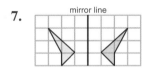

8. (a) The shapes cover a surface without overlapping and leaving no gaps.
  (b)

9. (a) *a* = 58°   (vertically opposite angles)
  (b) *b* = 155°   (supplementary angles)
  (c) *c* = 150°   (angles at a point)

10. (a) *A* (2, 3)   (b) *C* (−2, −1)
  (c) *D* (−2, 3)

11. (a) (i)

  A 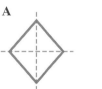   **B**

  C   **D**

  (ii) Place a mirror on the dotted line to see if the reflection is the same as the actual image.
  (b) (i) **TRUE**   (ii) **FALSE**
    (iii) **FALSE**   (iv) **TRUE**

12. 32 km

13. (a) 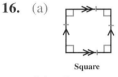   **14.**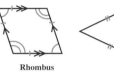

Not full size

15. (a) *a* = 67°   Angles in a triangle add to 180°.
  (b) *b* = 54°   Isosceles Δ.
          b = 180° − (2 × 63°).
  (c) *c* = 126°   Angles in a quadrilateral add to 360°.
          c = 180° − (360° − 306°)

16. (a)

    Square   Rhombus   Kite
  (b) Square, rectangle
  (c) Square

17. (a) E.g.   (b) E.g.

18. 25 litres

19. (a) (i) 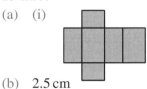   (ii) 46 cm²

  (b) 2.5 cm

20. (a) (i) *p* = 52   (ii) *q* = 76
  (b) Alternate angles

21. (a) (i) 5 cm   (ii) 100 km
  (b) (i) 060°   (ii) 240°

22. (a) *a* = 40°, *b* = 95°, *c* = 135°
  (b) *d* = 40°

23. (a) Reflection in the line *x* = 5.
  (b) Rotation, 90° anticlockwise, about (0, 0).
  (c) (i)

    (ii) 3 units to the right and 2 units down.

24. Height 175 cm,   weight 70 kg.

25. (a) 18 cm²   (b) 31 cm²

26.

27. 201 cm²

28. 3 km

29. (a) Ext. $\angle = \dfrac{360°}{6} = 60°$.

$a = $ int. $\angle = 180° - 60° = 120°$

(b) $b = 15°$

30. (a) 346 cm   (b) 7977 cm²

SECTION 28

Exercise 28   Page 62

1. (a) Laila   (b) Ria

(c) Corrin.
Pupils are in the same class and June is a later month in the school year than the other months given.

2. E.g.

Resort	Tally
Cervinia	IIII II
Livigno	IIII II
Tonale	IIII IIII

3. (a) E.g. May play a different sport. May play more than one of these sports. Answer does not indicate which sport is played.

(b) Which sport(s) do you play?

Football ☐   Rugby ☐   Hockey ☐

Netball ☐   Swimming ☐   Tennis ☐

Other ☐ (state) ………… None ☐

4. (a)

Weight range (w)	Tally	Frequency
$30 \leqslant w < 40$	IIII	4
$40 \leqslant w < 50$	IIII II	7
$50 \leqslant w < 60$	IIII II	7
$60 \leqslant w < 70$	IIII III	8
$70 \leqslant w < 80$	I	1
$80 \leqslant w < 90$	IIII	3

(b) $60 \leqslant w < 70$

5. E.g.

Year	M/F	Breakfast today	2 years ago
10	M	Cereal, toast	less
11	F	Grapefruit, yogurt	more
11	F	Toast	same
11	M	Boiled egg, toast	same

6. (a)

	Theatre	Art gallery	Science museum	Totals
Girls	11	9	7	27
Boys	8	2	13	23
Totals	19	11	20	50

(b) 7

7. No.   Men: $\dfrac{180}{200} = 90\%$ Women: $\dfrac{240}{300} = 80\%$

Higher proportion of men can drive.

SECTION 29

Exercise 29   Page 65

1. (a) (i) 60   (ii) 80

(b)

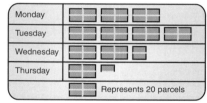

2. (a)

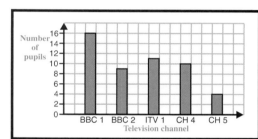

(b) 20%

3. (a) Each team played 25 matches.

(b) Range: 2,   mode: 2

(c) Women's team had a larger range (5) and higher mode (3).

4. (a) 12   (b) 22°C   (c) 14°C   (d) 15°C

5.

Country	USA	France	Spain	Greece
Angle	126°	90°	99°	45°

SECTION 30

Exercise 30   Page 66

1. (a) 7 cm   (b) 10 cm

(c) 11 cm   (d) 11.3 cm

2. (a) 12 goals   (b) 14 goals

3. (a) 5.3   (b) 5

(c) 9

4. (a) £9 (b) £10.50 (c) £11.50
(d) Median.
Mode is the lowest price and mean is affected by the one higher-priced meal.

5. (a) (i) 4.9 hours
(ii) 6 hours
(b) Last year there was a much bigger variation in the number of hours of sunshine each day and a lower average.

6. 38 points

7. (a) 5
(b) 9
(c) Reg: mean; Reg 9, Helen 8.6
Helen: mode; Reg 9, Helen 10
Friend: median; Both 9

8. (a) (i) 1 (ii) 3 (iii) 3.35
(b) Mode **and** median

SECTION 31

Exercise 31 — Page 69

1. (a)
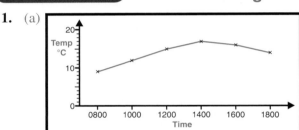
(b) 8°C
(c) (i) 16°C
(ii) Actual temperatures are only known at times when readings are taken.

2. (a)

Weight (w grams)	Tally	Frequency
$490 \leqslant w < 495$	$\|\|$	2
$495 \leqslant w < 500$	ⅢⅢ Ⅲ| |	11
$500 \leqslant w < 505$	ⅢⅢ |	6
$505 \leqslant w < 510$	ⅢⅢ |||	8
$510 \leqslant w < 515$	|||	3

(c) $495 \leqslant w < 500$

3. (a)
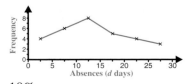
(b) 10%

4. Vertical scale is not uniform.
Balls do not match scale.

SECTION 32

Exercise 32 — Page 70

1. (a) (i) *C* (ii) *A* (iii) *B* (b) *C*

2. (a) 36 (b) 60 (c) No
(d) Yes (e) Positive

3. (b) Negative correlation.
As engine size increases, the time taken to travel 500 m decreases.
(c) 18 seconds

4. (b) Positive correlation.
As the average midday temperature increases the number of visitors increases.
(c) (ii) Points are close to the line of best fit.
(d) 12.5 thousand

SECTION 33

Exercise 33 — Page 73

1. (a) **C** (b) **B**

2.

S		H		N
0		$\frac{1}{2}$		1

3. (a) $\frac{1}{8}$ (b) $\frac{4}{8} = \frac{1}{2}$ (c) $\frac{5}{8}$

4. (a)

Ways to score a total of 6.	
Number on red dice	**Number on blue dice**
1	5
2	4
3	3
4	2
5	1

(b) Total score of 6.
There are five ways to score a total of 6.
Only one way to score a total of 12,
ie. (Red 6) + (Blue 6)

5. (a) 2, 3, 3, 4, 5.
Numbers 2, 3, 4, 5 have occurred and 3 has occurred twice as often as other numbers.
(b) 100. One chance in five of getting a 5.
$\frac{1}{5} \times 500 = 100$

6. 0.14

7. (a) 0.1 (b) 0.7

Section Review — Page 74

1. (a) 4   (b) 11   (c) 22

2. (a)

Number of pets	Tally	Frequency
0	IIII	4
1	HHI III	8
2	HHI	5
3	III	3
4	IIII	4
5	I	1

(b)

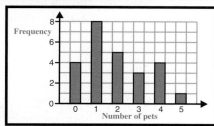

3. (a) (i) **TRUE**
    (ii) **FALSE**
    (iii) **TRUE**

(b) Conduct traffic surveys outside schools in different locations at the same time of day, for the same period of time, on the same day.

4. (a) 3   (b) 4   (c) 6   (d) 5

5. (a) (i) Blue
    (ii) Blue has only one sector.
    Red has seven sectors and Black has four sectors.

(b)

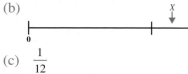

(c) $\frac{1}{12}$

6. (a) 20   (b) 6   (c) 5

(d)

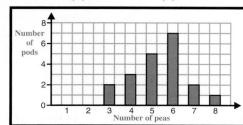

7. Vertical scale does not begin at zero, so improvements are exaggerated.

8. (a) $\frac{12}{25}$ (b) $\frac{5}{25} = \frac{1}{5}$

9. (a) £600   (b) £200

10. (a) 3   (b) 30   (c) 60

11. (a) (i)

Pantomime	Angle
Aladdin	135°
Cinderella	105°
Jack and the Bean Stalk	75°
Peter Pan	45°

    (ii) Aladdin

(b) (i) 72   (ii) $33\frac{1}{3}\%$

12. (a)

×	1	2	3	4
1	1	2	3	4
2	2	4	6	8
3	3	6	9	12

(b) $\frac{2}{12} = \frac{1}{6}$

(c) $\frac{4}{12} = \frac{1}{3}$

13. (a) A: Tuff hatchback
    B: Ace supermini
    C: Nippy sports
    D: Mega estate

(b) Nippy sports

14. 7.6

15. Ask what foods they ate **today** in the school canteen. Give choices to tick.

16. (a) $\frac{2}{5}$ (b) 0.6

17. (a)

```
                            4|5  means 4.5 cm
4 | 5  8  8
5 | 0  0  4  4  5  8
6 | 0  2  4  5  5  5  6  8
7 | 0  2  4
```

(b) 2.9 cm   (c) 6.1 cm

18. (a) $\frac{17}{75}$ (b) Yes. Female: $\frac{12}{50} = 24\%$

    Male: $\frac{5}{25} = 20\%$

19. (a) 1   (b) 2   (c) 2.2

Non-calculator Paper — Page 78

1. (a) Six thousand seven hundred and forty
(b) 6700
(c) 7 hundreds, 700

2. (a) 170

(b)

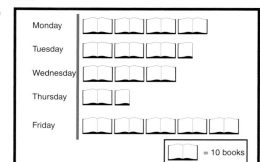

3. (a) 7, 12, 17   (b) 91, 82, 73

4. (a) 7, 19, 30, 105, 2002
    (b) (i) 75   (ii) 133   (iii) 286

5. (a) Shade any 12 squares.
    (b) (i) 0.6   (ii) 60%
    (c) (i) 31 302   (ii) 14 000
    (d) $100 \times 60 = 6000$

6. (a) 4   (b) 27
    (c) 64   (d) 13 and 27

7. (a) West   (b) North-West

8. 10

9. (a) (i) 2   (ii) 1
    (b) 16 cm   (c) 8 cm²

10.

Cola	£3.39
Potatoes	£0.75
Total	£4.14

11. (a) £37   (b) 15 days

12. (a)

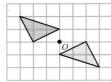

    (b) $(3, -2)$

13. (a) 20 miles   (b) 24 km

14. (a) Add 6 to the last number. 33
    (b) Double the last number. 32

15. $10 - x$ metres

16. (a) 3   (b) 4
    (c)

17. $P = 26$

18. (b) $QR = 5.7$ cm   (c) $\angle QRP = 39°$

19. (a) $\dfrac{3}{10}$ (b) 70%

20. (a) 43 914   (b) 30.5

21. **A:** 4, **B:** 2, **C:** 2

22. (a) 10 degrees   (b) $-3°C$

23. (a) $\dfrac{1}{2}$ (b) $\dfrac{7}{20}$

24. 1.05 pm

25. (a) (i) $a = 145°$
        (ii) Supp. $\angle$'s, $a + 135° = 180°$.
    (b) (i) $b = 83°$
        (ii) Angles in triangle sum to 180°.
    (c) (i) $c = 35°$
        (ii) Vertically opposite angles.

26. (a) (i) 3.28   (ii) 5.4
    (b) -6

27. 2.8 pence

28. (a) (i) $3a - 2$ (ii) $6a^2$ (iii) $2a + 3b$
    (b) (i) $x = -2$ (ii) $x = 4$ (iii) $x = 2.5$

29. (a) 220 cm²   (b) 300 cm³

30.

> 3 cloves of garlic
> 6 ounces of chick peas
> 6 tablespoons of olive oil
> 7.5 fluid ounces of Tahina paste

31. (a) $\angle BAC = 38°$
    (b) (i) 4   (ii) 1

32. (a) 0.78   (b) 0.3, $\dfrac{8}{25}$, 33%, $\dfrac{1}{3}$
    (c) 31

33. (a) 34   (b) 25

34. $\dfrac{3}{8}$

35. (a) X 1, X 3, Y 1, Y 3
    (b) Numbers 1 and 3 are not equally likely.

36. (a) 10   (b) 1 : 6

37. (a) 22 pounds   (b) £2.07

38. (a) 18 cm   (b) 12 cm²

39. (a) 25%   (b) 90

40. 60 km/h

41. (a)   (b)

42. (a) $11y - x$ (b) $5x + 15$
    (c) $A = -7$
    (d) (i) $x = 6$ (ii) $x = 1.5$

43. $a = 75°$, $c = 75°$

44. (a) 0.7   (b) 0.44

45. (a) $x = 60°$ (b) $y = 120°$

46. (a) 26   (b) 85%

47. (a) $\dfrac{50 \times 200}{4} = 2500$ (b) $1\dfrac{11}{12}$

48.

1. (a) 5   (b) 3570
    (c) Four tenths

2. (a) -7, -1, 0, 5, 13   (b) 20

3.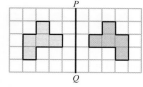

4. (a) Spain   (b) 12   (c) 51

5. (a) (i) £4.20   (ii) £5.80
    (b) 600 grams

6. (a)
Pattern number 4

    (b)

Pattern number	1	2	3	4	5
Number of matchsticks	5	9	13	17	21

    (c) Pattern number 10
    (d) (i) 401
       (ii) Multiply the Pattern number by 4 and add 1.

7. (a) **A** and **D**   (b) **Q**

8. £205

9. (a) Metres   (b) 12 m

10. (a) 53 minutes   (b) 0739

11. Turns through 180° in a clockwise direction.

12. 20

13. (a) 200 cm   (b) 2500 cm²

14. (a) 62.5   (b) 6   (c) 6

15. (a) (i) 1.73   (ii) 0.216
    (b) $m = 142.8$

16.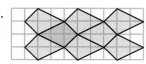

17. (a) 684 dollars   (b) £6

18. (a) 4 g
    (b) (i) $n = 4$ (ii) $m = 3$
    (c) 18

19. 36.25 km

20. E.g.

21. (a) −9   (b) 5   (c) $3(x - 2)$

22. £237.60

23. (a) 4.29   (b) 4.27

24. Yes. Glasses: $20 \times \frac{1}{3} = 6\frac{2}{3}$ pints
      Milk: $4 \times 1\frac{3}{4} = 7$ pints

25. (a) 36   (b) 12.5%

26. 24.1 kg

27. 80%, $\frac{7}{8}$, $\frac{8}{9}$, 0.9

28.

Soup	Angle
Chicken	120°
Mushroom	60°
Tomato	75°
Vegetable	105°

29. 58.8 kg

30. $a = 62°$, $b = 60°$, $c = 135°$

31. (a) 15   (b) 28 g
    (c) 30 g   (d) 29.3 g

32. Small. Small: $\frac{180}{36} = 5$ g/p
          Large: $\frac{300}{63} = 4.76$ g/p

33. (a) 56.5 cm   (b) 201 cm²

34. $\frac{1}{15}$

35. (a) 60 cm   (b) $d = \frac{a + b}{3}$

36. £10.80

37. (a) 10.94 yards   (b) 9.14 metres

38. 63 m²

39. 80

40. (a) 0815
    (b) (i) Between 0820 and 0835. Steepest gradient.
       (ii) 12 km/h

41. (a)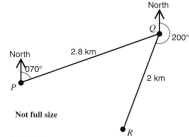

Not full size

    (b) 2.15 km, 295°

42. 1260°

43. (a) $y = 7$ (b) $p = 2.5$
    (c) $t = 3$

44. (b) Negative correlation.
      Countries with higher birth rates tend to have a lower life expectancy.
    (d) 52 to 57

45. $x = 20$

Index